❧ *The* ❧
GRAB

The GRAB

by
MARIA KATZENBACH

William Morrow and Company, Inc.
New York
1978

Printed in the United States of America.

1   2   3   4   5   6   7   8   9   10

Library of Congress Cataloging in Publication Data

Katzenbach, Maria.
The grab.

I. Title
PZ4.K19677Gr [PS3561.A778]   813'.5'4   77-3722
ISBN 0-688-03216-8

BOOK DESIGN   CARL WEISS

THIS BOOK IS DEDICATED TO

MY MOTHER, L.P.S.K.,

AND TO THE MEMORY

OF HER MOTHER,

E.K.P.S.

1885–1973

AUTHOR'S NOTE

❦

The objects in the house are all copied from the inventory my grandmother had made three years before her death.

With the single exception of the inventory, all objects and subjects are fiction.

Mighty magic is a mother,
in her there is another issue
of fixture, repeated form, the race renewal,
the charge of the command.

—ROBERT CREELEY

Every wise woman buildeth her house;
But the foolish plucketh it down with her hands.

—Proverbs 14:1

THE GRAB

❦

PROLOGUE

FIRST FLOOR

SECOND FLOOR

IN THE BEDS THEY HAD AS CHILDREN

THE DEATH PAPERS

THE LOVE LETTERS

BOOKLINED

A ROUND OF STILLS

PHILOSOPHICAL OBJECTS

TRESPASSING

THIRD FLOOR

SLEEP

GOING

GOING

GONE (Epilogue)

❧ *The* ❧
GRAB

❧ PROLOGUE ❧

THE
PRAYER

THE MOTHER GIVES TO EACH DAUGHTER A PART OF HER NAME, and during her life each daughter takes the name as her own until three separate names grow from one name. The Mother gives to each daughter a part of her face, and during her life she watches her own features transforming in the three separate faces, the faces of her daughters gradually changing into the faces of three other women. And to each daughter the Mother gives a part of her mind. During her life she sees the thread of her own intellect unravel into three separate strands as each daughter holds onto hers not as a gift from the Mother, but as her own refined cord.

But her body must give up living, as it is now, before what the Mother did not give is divided by the grab.

"Damn the sun," she curses. "Damn four o'clock," when the sun hits the window of her bedroom shooting the reflections into her eyes. It's painful to move. She reaches her arms, the wrinkled flesh hanging like loose skeins of wound wool, to the swollen leg. Then, holding her breath, she shifts her weight, which is not the weight of a body, and turns this sheath wrapped in layers of white organdy. One of the feather pillows now presses against her neck. She tries slowly to sit up, but pain in her abdomen jerks her down. Her head drops. She breathes out.

"A prayer," she begins, "is not a prayer when it asks for something. This is not a prayer. It is a confession: If I wish to die, I am already dead." She is talking to her god and her disease. As she continues to pray in her precise language of final business and tied-up ends, the sun turns the bedroom to gold fringed with copper. Around her body, a body of what surgeons had not scooped out, the spaces of the bedroom grow. Flat brocades are thrown into relief. Dull blooms ornament. Yellowed threads burn to ocher as the words of the woman fall into the sun's falling, as the prayer shines obliquely on the walls, and the sound of her voice comes down over the inert arms of the chaise. The posts of the bed listen, alerted by the last recitation.

There are no stories left. There is no time for stories. Only the passing in and out of generations in the rooms, invasions of the inherited house, trespassing where my portrait hangs on my walls.

The relatives have told their stories. My husband's story has been told: Twenty years in bed. Pills. Shots. Hospital rooms. A dead story of medicine prescribed, medicine taken.

The jewelry has already been divided. I have watched three pairs of hands handle the rings, loop the pearls, covet the stones.

The plants have been watered. The latch on the gate is fixed. The diary is closed.

My story is not my story. I am the property accounted for,
the inventory that has been made. Typed, it lies on the desk.

Her hands fall to her lap. On the table beside the chaise is
the shut diary; next to the diary, her Bible. She looks at the
Bible, reaches out, then lets her arm drop. Looking at the
diary, she hesitates. Her arm reaches to it. She takes the
leatherbound notebook, and, placing it in her lap, she opens
it to the first page, although she knows what is written there.
She reads to herself: "Two days ago I gave birth to my
second daughter. A difficult birth." She closes the diary. "It
will stay closed," she thinks. She leaves the diary in her lap.
Then, pain. She presses the diary against herself, as if to
relieve the pain. It increases, sharp. She lifts the diary from
her lap and lets it drop. "A diary is for the others, living."
Over thirty years ago the doctor said that the growth in
her uterus was not malignant. He did say that it would be
malignant in the future. So remove the uterus, the growth;
remove the word, life.
But cells are cunning. Cut out the nest and they migrate
to another place. Waiting thirty years, gathering their forces,
they program their nuclei for the attack in timed intervals
at designated areas. Then they sprout tumors in the full,
round places on her body, mocking her female form. Her
breast, cheek, her hip, and now the cells attack her origins,
penetrate into the folds of her glands, dig into walls of
tissue.

The motion of generations is pain. "Mother," my second
daughter asked, before the hospital gave me up for dead and
sent me home, "Mother, if you could have done anything
differently, what would it have been?" Animals are born.
Human beings are born to ask, Would you have loved me?

I would have given birth to human beings who from the beginning could speak and think. But that is unnatural birth. The natural birth is the birth of blubbering spineless animals who crawl and cry and sleep, who wet the nurse's arm, poke their fingers in the mush, and lie in their cradle wobbling like junket in a dish.

Children are not made in the image of God. Children are made in the image the man and woman have of flesh. The parent civilizes the offspring. When they learn to speak, they learn to distinguish error.

I have accounted for all my mistakes but one. I answered her question. For this I cannot account.

The sun glows red. She looks at the pinkly glowing walls, at the pink tips of her fingers, and, suddenly, her bitterness overwhelms her. She wants to take back the confession, certain that the disease and God have heard. Always her body, always her body lies between her and God. The woman cannot escape her body. It is made to repeat itself, to fill and to empty.

You and the disease feed my hatred of my body.
You and the disease interfere, trespassing where you are not wanted. Kill me. Kill me whom you have already killed.

As the sun disappears and the reflections vanish, her mind and body cool. The narrow time of the day returns to her. She has not eaten. The food she puts into her mouth only comes back up. She is wearing the nightgown and robe she slept in. The organdy is crushed. She brushed her cloud of hair this morning, and now the wisps have settled around her head which she turns from one wall to the other, from one texture to the next. The pattern on the bedcover becomes a face, a face she does not know. She will speak to this face before she expires.

She lifts her pale arms into the mixed light and dark of twilight. Fingering an organdy sleeve delicately, as one would stroke the wings of a bird to calm the bird, she detains the flight.

I want to flee the trinity of daughters I have made.
I see four faces in the one face of the portrait. One face was painted in 1885, the year I was born. At every birth the portrait was repainted. I remember the dates they were born; but I do not know how old my daughters are. The subtractions and additions of their lives is not the time I know.

Downstairs in the hall hangs the portrait painted when she was forty-four. The portrait does not resemble the woman lying upstairs in the dark. The painting looks exactly like her youngest daughter, Sadie. The painting is hers. The painting, according to the Code, is her eldest daughter's, Barbara's, her namesake. The painting is her second daughter's, Louisa's, who finds meaning in gifts beyond the Code.

She looks over to the bedcover, and, seeing the face, wonders if it will speak to her. Will it decide for her this last decision? She wants only to be rid of images, to unpaint the portrait, to discard all references to her physical existence. If only the portrait would leave when she leaves. If only the portrait would not remain as the Code remains.

But the portrait has already been given away. Her intellect, now, spins itself out into the rampant light as the walls of the room deepen to scarlet to purple and finally into black shadow. Who are you? She turns her eyes toward the face that will be—but the movement is imperceptible, the face gone. As all sense of motion drains from her head, escaping through her fingertips, her face drains white and disappears. Numb. Her hand, invisible in the boxed shadow, the room, floats at the borders of her white sleeve. Only her white sleeve, and the layers of her white robe, visit the dark with a light of their own. Around her head framing the porcelain skull her fragile hair stills the air. Where am I?

I am in the room, and—now—I am the room.

Suddenly a pain in her chest explodes. Particles of light escape from her eyes. Her head opens. Purified, bleached to spirit, to snow, cool dry snow falls, descending from the sky into the cup of her mind past her eyes, as the vision is stripped of color, past her throat, as the words are stripped of images, into her heart. She freezes. Then slowly she begins to rise.

She floats, hovering like the moon in the dark bedroom, floating, a suspension of spirit suspended; then, slowly, she ascends into the black, open zero, an ice-cold, blue-lipped angel.

THE
LIVING ROOM

D OWNSTAIRS IN THE LIVING ROOM SIT THREE WOMEN—SISTERS and wives and mothers and daughters—talking. It is an early November morning, and the light spreads in an even wash over the heavy burden of their talk. "Mother," says Sadie, "did not want a funeral service of any kind. So I think that, I really think that we have to respect her last wishes. I mean, it's only fair."

"We must do something," Barbara says in her deep voice. "Mother is dead. She has been dead for three days."

"I know, Barbara, I know," Sadie says, as if she did not know. "I just wanted to tell you both what you might not understand—that Mother did not want a service. She thought that it was excessive and indulgent. I am not," Sadie looks directly at her other sister, "expressing my own opinion. I'm only telling you what Mother felt."

Louisa responds with silence. Barbara echoes the silence. Her patience with Sadie, who has talked constantly these

23

past three days about what Mother said, Mother thought, Mother felt, what Mother told *her,* has expired. Barbara wants everything to run smoothly. The absence of reply from her two sisters makes Sadie blink.

Hysterical denial, Louisa observes as she watches Sadie fold and unfold her fingers, bending them into her lap to depress the middle-aged fat. *I must listen to what they are saying. If I hear my sisters speaking to me we will overcome —there is a chance we will overcome—the distance between us. But I feel as alone as I have always felt in their company.*

Barbara: We must keep things in order. Time, activity, sorting and gathering—these things we must insist on now.

Sadie: I will scream.

"We must come to a decision no later than noon," Barbara pronounces. "We can't waste any time. The best thing for us to do is to lay our cards on the table, and concentrate on the issue at hand: Are we going to have a funeral service or not? That's what we have to talk about.

"Personally," Barbara continues, placing her sentence in front of Sadie's eyes, "I feel that it isn't going against Mother's wishes—"

"Is or isn't?" Sadie interrupts.

"I said, is not going against Mother's wishes, for she did tell me something slightly different from what you say she told you, Sadie—" Sadie smiles. *There will be no funeral.* ". . . having a small family service. It was that we would let some preacher who didn't even know Mother say some big fancy words about God and heaven that she couldn't stand. But I honestly think that she would have thought that a family service was quite in order. Part of the Code."

"Oh, yes," chimes Sadie, eager to change the subject. "The Code. How Mother loved the Code. Do you remember, you two, when she met Maggie's beau? I know I'll never forget it. Maggie was, of course, the first grandchild—and the only grandchild—to get married. I was so afraid of what Mother would think of his appearance, so I tried, you know, to soften the blow." Sadie smiles, and leans back, her hands flat on her thighs. "So, I thought that the easiest thing to do would be, you know, to change chairs during lunch, after every course, so that it wasn't until dessert that Mother found Mark sitting next to her. I was on the other side. And she leaned over, I'll never, never forget it, she leaned over and said to me, 'We do have our Code, you know,' and then she turned to Mark and was so charming, and careful, of course, not to mention his background and all of that, which—"

"Sadie, I'm sure that Louisa and I will never forget your luncheon of musical chairs," Barbara says. Another cheerful anecdote from Sadie and she will stop trying to be diplomatic. "You don't need to tell us that story now. We know it only too well."

"I was just trying to make light of all this gloom," Sadie says, but without accusation, and without recognition of the increasing heaviness of her sister's will tightening the air around her. There is no gloom; there is only her oldest sister. Suddenly, Sadie laughs. "I do remember what she said if"— Sadie leans forward— "if we should decide to have a service." She looks at the others, waiting. Louisa has not moved. Barbara shifts her weight in the chair.

"Yes?"

"Well," Sadie begins with a sigh which instantly bounces up into a breath. "I know this will cheer both of you!" She sits at the edge of the chair. "A few days before, you know, Mother said that there were two things she absolutely would not tolerate. This was in the hospital, when I was taking my turn watching over her. (*Louisa, listening: It's uncanny. I wonder if she can hear herself doing it.*) First, she said she

would not have any flowers. 'I won't have any florist perfuming my funeral,' she said in that wonderful singing voice.
You know," Sadie tilts her head, "it was funny with Mother
about singing. She would never sing herself, though she
adored music, particularly piano music. She would always
say to me, 'Choir practice? I thought it was the spirit that
moved you to song.' (*Barbara: Digressions, stories, idiocy.
She doesn't see. But then again, she never has.*) Where was
I?" Sadie presses her fingers to her lips. "Oh yes. The other
thing. The other thing she said was typical, just typical of
Mother. 'I've managed to avoid church all these years,' she
said. 'A fact of which I am extremely proud. I will not have
you spoiling my success after I've gone. If you must have a
service, do me the service of having it as far from any church
as you possibly can.' Those were her very words—you know,
'service,' and 'service.' I remember when she said them I
thought about how sad it was that Mother never reconciled
herself to the church. But you two don't know about that
kind of thing, do you? I don't mean," Sadie says, alarmed,
"that you're insensitive, and I certainly don't mean that
Mother was insensitive. Not at all! At all! It's just that she
could sometimes sound that way, though I know she didn't
mean it." Sadie leans back, looks out the window. "You
know?" She turns to face both of her sisters. The blue of her
eyes expands. "Deep down in her heart Mother was extremely
religious. It was a private thing with her." Sadie seems, at
last, to have stopped talking.

Louisa finally speaks into the silent space. "That suits me,"
she says.

"What do you think," Barbara asks stiffly, "of a service—
in general, I mean, how do you look at such things?"

"What do I think?" Louisa crosses her arms in front of her,
then, realizing her defense, forces her hands down to her lap.

"Well," she begins. "I don't know what I think, really. But I do know what I feel." Louisa finds her arms have quickly returned to their defensive position. "I feel that a funeral is not something for the dead. It is for the living. It is a chance for reunion, a coming together of the family and all the people who loved the person who died. I mean," she avoids the friction of Sadie's eyes, "we should be sad. We should be sad together. It's the only way we have of knowing that the person is dead—by mourning together. A funeral is a ritual for our sadness, our grief." Louisa's even voice now breaks as she presses more rapidly the point she is uncertain of until articulated. "It's so important that we do allow ourselves to feel sad over what is a large, large loss, yes, loss. Death just isn't happy. It's very—well, very painful, yes, it is, Sadie, it is painful, no matter what—"

"Why are you saying that to me?"

"Because I—well, we're the ones, all three of us and the rest of the family, we're left here with the pain. And I—"

Sadie: Always intellectualizing just to cover up. Mother lived

"Mother lived a full life, Louisa," Sadie says. Louisa now reaches for a cigarette. "And I feel—I feel that we should be able to celebrate her full life, by remembering her with joy." On the last word Sadie twists her mouth obstinately around the vowel.

"I am happy that she lived a full life," Louisa says as the smoke streams out between them, catching the light evenly like a blank reel. "And God knows it was a full life."

"Yes," Barbara says into the smoke. "Unusually full for a woman of her time."

"Yes," Sadie says, smiling. "Not peculiar, though."

"Well," Louisa begins, then changes course: "I'm not deny-
ing that she lived an interesting life. I always thought that
she left a lot unsaid, you know, all kinds of things which she
didn't like to explain or talk about. But that's neither here
nor there. When a woman who did live such a great life dies,
we should feel particularly sad at our loss."

"Of course," Sadie says from the other side of the now
trailing lines of smoke, sifting the tight air of the room.
"Of course we're sad that she's no longer with—"

"That she's dead," Barbara says flatly.

"Yes, Barbara, I know," Sadie says, and then, without
pausing, she jerks out, "But we should act as if—as if she
were here." She opens her eyes onto Barbara. "Shouldn't
we?"

She is there, sitting in three chairs. She is moving there in
the tight air as the daughters shift positions in the chairs,
look at each other through the smoke and say Mother is dead
Mother is not dead. They turn to the open door. Quickly
they glance at the empty hallway imagining Mother standing
and listening to their talk. Their imaginations do not deceive
them. The smoke veils them from one another, but Mother
is standing in that white atmosphere making decisions, conducting as she always did.

"We must make a decision," Barbara says, prompted by
the nodding smoke. Barbara nods herself to Sadie, who ab-
sently nods in return. Louisa retreats. "Well," Barbara pulls
herself forward, resettling into her seat. "It seems that there
is no real objection to having a service on the conditions
that there are no flowers from a florist and no church
nearby."

Louisa bursts out laughing. She is not laughing at Barbara,
who sits back suddenly; she is laughing at the sober tones of

Barbara's voice as she pronounced the no-flower, no-church funeral.

How impossibly prejudiced Mother was. I remember her wrinkled nose and pursed lips when I was fifteen and going out on my first date. I had pinned a corsage to my dress. Mother looked down at it, and, in front of my date, she said, "Don't you think you smell sweet enough without that large clump on your chest?" I was so embarrassed that at the first opportunity I slipped into the powder room and doused myself from head to toe in perfume. At the next dance the poor boy sneezed so violently that we had to sit down.

"What's so funny?" Barbara asks.

"It is funny, isn't it? To think of how Mother hated flowers from a florist? I mean, it's terribly funny." All three daughters gradually, without knowing what is funny, begin to laugh. Then the laughter suddenly releases into convulsions as they rock in their chairs. The velvet and the thick Flemish tapestry on the wall absorb the laughter issuing from their three bodies.

The body of the youngest daughter is one plump circular shape. Inside the circle the flesh balloons, and like a balloon Sadie's body gives when pressed lightly, then buoys back. She is a buoy in the air, bobbing gently, gently protected by her dry, evenly pink layer of skin. In her face all of her features— blue eyes, puffy cheeks and receding chin—are hugged by blond curls. Just as one always thinks that a baby smiles, one always thinks Sadie smiles. But her face forces the happiness to its surface; for behind that constant smile her mouth leads like ruins to the hollowed-out throat.

Louisa is the openly silent one. Her silence, like the dark

hair on her head, works as a thin cover for the full words within. It is her body that is the shadow, masked by the brightly colored clothes she wears. Their rich textures hide a body that bears children with difficulty. Her hips are tight. Her breasts filled with powdered milk. She tries to soften the bony structure of her face with creamy makeup, moisturizers, and she exaggerates her large brown eyes with different shades of eyeliners. But if one could see into the center of her eyes, one would see a bleak pupil reflecting the light around her, extremely sensitive to its gradations. To look at Louisa's eyes is to look at something missing. Louisa depends on the shadings of her intuition to interpret the lights but also to hide her body from her own inward stare. When she does break the silence, though, her words fall in rational beats over her prominent bones.

Barbara's body is always ready to go someplace—she doesn't know where: Outside, just outside. Her face, well scrubbed, meets the air directly at cheeks and jaw. She is an athlete, well proportioned, proud of her physical strength. She is in "top form" at age fifty-three. Her face, like Sadie's, resembles Mother's, but without the aura that Mother had. Barbara is real to a fault; too down to earth. She walks with her heels planted firmly into the ground, measuring her steps. When she enters a room and places herself, she gives the impression of occupying the space with certainty and deliberation. But she also gives the impression that she will leave any moment, and she doesn't know when. She cannot help it. Whenever she feels that she wants to leave, she grips the arms of her chair and sits, fixed, imposing her authority on the air.

These are the bodies of the daughters.

The bodies of the wives are the bodies of a pillow, a sapling and a new boxspring. As a mother, Sadie is the song sung to her children to inhibit the thrill of the moon—but its melody celebrates its luminous craters. Louisa, as a mother, is the reassuring mind keeping a nightly vigil over her children's nightmares. Barbara is the mother who is the teammate, the worldly companion who sleeps in foreign nights in distant time zones, but always returns to tell her children a story.

These three bodies, sitting in their mother's living room, are in one way blind. The only bodies they can see are the bodies sitting in chairs like the objects, the other bodies, in the room. The only movements they see are the apparent movements of each other: Louisa lighting one cigarette after another; Sadie kneading her fingers in her lap; Barbara resting her arms on the arms of the chair, gripping at the edge. None of the daughters can see clearly the other object— Mother—as she is: waiting to be cremated and buried in a stone jar next to the two-years-interred ashes of her husband, Phillip, their father. Instead, the daughters see blindly another body moving in the living room, where she cannot be but is. In the laughed-out silence of the room there is no doubt that Mother remains to make the air stuffy and the velvet cushions too hot. But no one suggests opening a window, or moving to the back room which looks out over the garden through a sliding glass wall. The most that anyone can do is to suggest, as Sadie now does, that she "get everyone a nice cold glass of ginger ale and maybe some cookies?"

Left alone together the two older sisters turn to face one another. "What can we do?" Barbara says to Louisa. "She's impossible. She won't let anyone get a word in edgewise. She acts as if Mother hadn't died, for God's sake. What is going on with her?"

All of their lives together the thin book-reading sister and the outgoing horseback rider have been opposed. Now they sit facing one another on the same side, but not together. For Louisa's well-informed statements, the way that she will, in a moment, talk through the question to another question with a new answer, will point out, as it has always pointed out, Barbara's imaginative failings. Barbara's health silently accused Louisa's underdeveloped body, and now Barbara's health again displays, in contrast, Louisa's delicate frame. They are and always were necessary to each other. And Sadie bounced between them, imitating, up at the lake the summers they were little girls, the loon's laugh with her hands cupped to her mouth better than they could; Sadie orbiting—off course—in the space between them, signaling with her cupped hands the laugh that made the young lake air tingle at night—was as necessary to them as the sun is necessary to light the moon.

Louisa begins to talk, knowing even as she speaks that she cannot give Barbara an answer to her question. Because Louisa knows that no matter how much she may wish to meet her sister on this side, she will, inevitably, answer the question in her own language, the only language she knows, but one that estranges her from her sister—and from Sadie. Louisa sees that Barbara wants a set of instructions, a code like Mother's Code, that will inform her of the situation and offer a way out. She does not want the words that Louisa is offering to her. For Louisa does not respond to situations; she responds only to their weaves, to the variegated pattern of motive and suppressed wish. Instead of sound principles, Louisa is wasting time talking about Sadie. *Barbara: How can she talk about Sadie's childhood when, in a moment, she will return and, with irrepressible cheerfulness, pass the cookies around?* As Louisa continues, Barbara envisions a hand rising up between them, crosshatched with age, the knuckles like knots on a barbed wire fence. It forbids change. It splits the air. It interferes. It is Mother's.

Sadie returns. Louisa has, from Barbara's point of view (on the other side of the hand), said nothing. Sadie offers her a cookie, "one of the sugar cookies that Mother was fond of—so fond of. I remember every Christmas we'd get a big box of them, and the girls would have eaten them all up before New Year's,"—

Barbara: Why can I hear Sadie's stories, which I cannot stand to hear, but cannot hear Louisa, whom I so want to hear? Mother, your hand deafens me. Mother, do not remove your hand.

"Well," Sadie says, sitting down, "well." She bites into a cookie, then dusts the crumbs off her breast onto the floor.

"Don't," Barbara says.

"Don't what?"

"Don't do that—you're messing up the Persian rug." Barbara points.

"So I am," Sadie says, and tries with her foot to rub the crumbs away.

"No, no, don't do that either." Sadie looks at Barbara, surprised. "I mean," Barbara says, "it doesn't make any difference now."

"Of course it makes a difference," Sadie says. "Why, it's impolite to spill crumbs on someone else's rug."

"It isn't someone else's," Louisa says flatly, who all morning has been careful to avoid spilling cigarette ashes on the rug. "It is no longer anyone's but belongs to one of us. Or it will belong to one of us," she says.

"The Persian rug?"

"Of course. It's not going to stay here."

"Well, how silly of me! Of course. It's just that I—well, it still belongs to—but I guess you're right," Sadie says, "I guess you're right."

The daughters pause to look around the living room as their eyes, opened by Louisa, begin to grab, one by one, the objects around them. Yes, Barbara thinks, the next step in this process is the grab. The grab is a family tradition that formerly the daughters collectively regarded with some humor and a vague disbelief that just the three of them would have to participate in one together. For generations the Luskins had written a clause in their wills which designated the persons who were to participate in what was called the grab. Usually restricted to the closest relatives still living, the grabs throughout the generations had only once been "open house." Great Aunt Mathilda, who lived on a large estate, allowed all brothers, sisters, grandchildren, even grandnephews and nieces, whoever could afford the transportation, to divide her property. Louisa, Barbara and Sadie had been there, but it seems so long ago that it feels to them like a distant childhood memory, though they were all recently married at the time. It was a great big party to them, standing in line with numbers for an entire day and night, partying at meals— more like a wake than a grab.

Mother had specified in her will that only her daughters could grab for her goods. Husbands, usually included, were excluded this time. She had bequeathed a few things; they had already divided the jewelry; she had left certain sums of money for close friends and servants. But the bulk of their mother's wealth had been left intentionally—though they did not know Mother's intention—for them to divide among themselves, according to a procedure of their own design. Though all of them knew before that Mother had made this decision, not until this moment do they each individually realize its pressure on them.

Before, Sadie thought of the tradition of the grab as sacrilegious. After Great Aunt Mathilda's grab, she had returned home feeling uncomfortable with what she had grabbed. The memory of relatives drinking and laughing lined up to choose from the house of her dead aunt to furnish their own houses with her things filled Sadie with petty horror. How could we have been so disrespectful of the dead? How could we have behaved as we did? But now, as her eyes alight on the distant chandelier over the dining room table, her mind changes. Now she thinks that the grab is only natural. Things would have to be given away anyway. One has to go on living. And besides, she feebly concludes, it's more an honor to the dead than a dishonor.

To Louisa the grab was a tradition that characterized, more than any other tradition, The Family. The grab was a personal ritual of greedy selves all after something—typical of the Luskin character that jealousies thought to be avoided were in fact incurred. In addition, the grab was an index to the family's wealth. Only a well-established upper-class family, who once led the New York Four Hundred, would come up with a way to display and remove their wealth simultaneously, feeling that too much was always a sin; too little equally reprehensible. But now Louisa sees the grab differently, particularly: as her eyes fall on the desk at which Mother wrote, she thinks, No, it's not the money, it's not The Family's wealth. We're greedy for some object to remember our special relationship to the dead. We're grabbing at the memory in the object, at what the object might mean to us individually.

In favor of most Luskin traditions, and a staunch defender of the Code, Barbara always accepted the grab without questioning—part of the body of lore Luskins delighted in passing from one generation to the next, embellishing with each new age. It was the way The Family spread their wealth, a form of succession. It was the way The Family's dead took care of the living. In her mind the grab did not differ significantly from a will with bequests. The grab certainly relieved the person making the will of countless decisions. But as Barbara observes the pattern of one thousand and one Buddhas on the wall panel imported from India, Barbara realizes that— though unlikely—it was still possible her mother would have given it to someone else, when Barbara is the one who should have it. Barbara now sees an underlying wisdom in leaving the choices to the survivors. She sees a deeper order than the superficial order of a will.

None of the daughters knows what they are all grabbing. Nor do they know what their grab will bring to them and take away from them.

Sadie now, suddenly, realizes that there is another feature to the grab, but she can't quite put her finger on it. All she knows is that she does want to have a funeral service, and as soon as possible. But where? She thinks hard. Then she remembers there's a chapel right next to the old park they played in as children, with the graveyard hidden on the other side of the hill.

"I know just where we can have it," Sadie says, delighted with herself.

"What?" Barbara says, roused by Sadie's high voice. "Have what?"

"Why, the service, of course. I know just the place," she says. "That chapel, you know . . ." Sadie is filled with the sound of the simple music (of her selection) that will echo in the chapel, the music that silences the scream. And this beautiful sound of her mother's service deafens Sadie utterly.

Louisa sits, smoking a cigarette, thinking that at last they

will be sad, remember, will mourn to make real their grief—
astonished that Sadie should lead them to this place.

And Barbara, though she realizes that the obstacle is now
mysteriously removed, forgets what Sadie obstructed; for the
clink in her drink sounds to Barbara like the small tinny
cowbells she heard on her trip, years ago, to India.

And none of her daughters hears Mother's voice pronounce:
Amen.

THE
EMPTY CHAPEL

OUTSIDE, SLOWLY, FROM ALL DIRECTIONS, THE LIVING BODY OF the Luskin family, through the serpentine paths of the park, three generations spiraling in to converge on the small oval chapel, with a peaked roof and one round rose window, embracing one another, guiding one another—once inside —with pointed solemnity down the strip of aisle, settling themselves in new lines of pews which divide generations and families, face the cordoned-off space of the missing body of Mother. Gathered together to mourn, comfort, remember and forget, they range from a just-full adolescent girl (Sadie's youngest) to an already-shrivelled great aunt (the legendary Adrian Luskin's widow), from the mascara-glossed to the cataract-jeweled merging into a pool of Luskin eyes. No tears or dark glasses betray their assembled gaze at nothing and the rose window. In the overcast light at the chapel doors the male eyes of husbands take on the Luskin radiance; and the open arms of receiving daughters and the dark shoulders of escorting husbands move in and out of the arriving mass of related limbs.

Few of The Family wear black. Great Aunt Carey is wearing mink. The bright green sleeves of Sadie's dress appear and disappear as revolving green stripes at others' waists. Louisa wears a soft gray wool dress, cabled; but even on her slight body her arms are constrained by the close sleeves. Barbara wears a navy suit, standing still beside her husband, Tom, a tall blond man whose features have sharpened into bold middle age. "They make a good couple," everyone said at their wedding. They still do.

Tom leans down to whisper in Barbara's ear. Avoiding Louisa's watchful eyes, Barbara pauses. Reaching up with her hand she kisses Tom on the cheek, only then turning to glance at Louisa behind his shoulder. Louisa sees her. Quickly she looks to see if Patrick, her husband, has seen this exchange. He has. He looks at his wife ironically, indicating in the way that he readjusts his poor-fitting suit that he, too, feels caught.

Not caught at a funeral (which is not a funeral but a meeting of people who all resemble one another too thoroughly, appearing like well-directed and carefully selected extras in a movie out of the film of the afternoon air, randomly, rehearsed in natural motions which belie their intricate ties). No. Patrick is caught in the delayed arrangements for separation. Over a month ago he and Louisa reached a decision. But then, immediately, Mother became ill and entered the hospital. She seemed intent on dying. And so, in a cool tone Louisa informed her husband that she would need him to see her through her mother's death. He was to understand that her death did not terminate their arrangements, it merely interfered. It was the pattern of their marriage that when Louisa demanded of him he submitted; she directed his actions toward her. But during the long silences when she would not speak Patrick moved freely. It is this static balance that has forced them apart.

Their appearance together at the funeral is close to their last act as a married couple. They have not yet announced to The Family their intentions to separate. That is, Louisa has said nothing. But Patrick has taken advantage of her silence to mention it to his brother-in-law, Tom. As he looks now at his wife he thinks of his betrayal. For Patrick knows that Barbara now knows, and that soon Sadie and George will know. A single sentence—"We're planning to separate when this all blows over"—quietly delivered in the hall on their way out of Mother's house cut into the root, and will spread through the Luskin branches. There are no secrets in that house. He takes pride in his knowledge of the workings of this family into which he married, wondering if his two brothers-in-law feel the same reversal he does: A woman should marry into her husband's family. But a man marries into the Luskin family; they all did.

Louisa stares past her husband, for whom she has no desire, to fix her eyes on a tree, following down the grooves of bark to the roots pawing the unhinged leaves.

"Looza?" she hears. "Looza? Is that you? My goodness, but you do get thinner every time I do see you."

Louisa turns, recognizing the melody. "Jewel." Her arms open. "How are you?"

"Well," Jewel says as her face moves in to kiss Louisa on the cheek. "I don't imagine any of us is feeling too good right now." Jewel is the Luskins' old maid; she has always been the old maid, before real age salted her hair and dried her cheeks into furrows.

"No," Louisa says, her hand in Jewel's. "No, this is a sad time."

"It surely is that, honey. You always was my favorite one, and my heart aches to see you so—so—" Suddenly one of Sadie's daughters appears at her side, urging Jewel into the chapel. As they turn from Louisa, Jewel's eyes try to finish her sentence, wondering what is really on Louisa's mind. Louisa, in response to Jewel's gaze, shrugs her shoulders; but they remain tucked against her neck as Louisa feels tears like vises pressing against her eyes.

"She looks terrible," Louisa says to Barbara, who has moved over beside her.

"I'd say you were the one who was in trouble."

"Trouble?" Louisa blinks.

"Yes. I'd call a divorce trouble."

"Not now, Barbara, not now."

"Why," Sadie rushes out the doors, "isn't that lovely? To see Jewel after all of these years. Of course, I've been writing to her regularly, to keep up with her health. As I'm sure you know, she has arthritis pretty bad."

"Does she?"

"Oh, Louisa! I was sure you would know about that."

At this moment, with the wives in a line, a car drives up the road to the entrance. They watch, curious, as a chauffeur gets out, goes around to the side door nearest them, and opens it. Gradually from behind the tall figure of the chauffeur a cane appears; then stiff tufts of white hair; a man's head; shoulders; the stooped body of a stranger. He shoves his cane at the chauffeur as at a stray dog, moving jerkily toward the women. As he approaches he lifts his head, just above the hook of the cane, and smiles broadly. His eyes are unmistakably Mother's. The wives stand without moving, without recognizing him.

"Barbara," he says, bowing from his already bent position. He moves sideways, like a crab, to Louisa. "Louisa." Stumb-

ling over his cane he stands before Sadie. "Sarah." He takes
a step back, breaking into laughter. "So she went first," he
mumbles as his cane shakes. "Don't know . . . know . . .
Come and go, never did like . . . it, never did like them
writing the goddamned letters . . . I never answered them
. . . Stopped. Stopped coming after a while. Good. Liked
that. Liked that." Suddenly he stops, and yells at Sadie, "My
sister in there?"

"Oh." Sadie's eyes open. "Oliver!"

"Well of course it's Oliver. Who the hell else would be
crazy enough to come to a family gathering without an invita-
tion? Who the hell else would—"

"Oliver," Barbara says calmly, moving close to him. He
recoils, hissing.

"None of that kissing stuff, none of that family kissing
stuff. Not for me. I asked you a question."

"No," Barbara says slowly. "She's dead, Oliver. I'm sorry—"

"I know she's *dead*. Have to watch. Have to keep watching
those obits. Never know but there might be one less Luskin.
Better than that goddamned Family News." He laughs. "Now,
I'll tell you," he leans on his cane, wobbling, "one day I'm
going to write a letter to the entire Luskin family, yes. And
I'll tell you just exactly what—"

"Let me take you in," Barbara says. Instantly Oliver quiets
and extends his free arm to her.

"That man!" Sadie says to Louisa. "How can he act that
way?"

"Don't pay any attention to it, Sadie. He doesn't know
what he's saying most of the time. And anyway, he's perfectly
harmless."

"But he's—" Sadie stops, catching the chauffeur's eye.
"You can move your car away, please," she yells to him. He
drops a cigarette and smiles with half his mouth.

Oliver was Mother's only sibling. When his sister married into the Luskin family, she had not lived at home for over ten years. Oliver never forgave his sister for running away —until she married into a wealthy family, one of the New York Four Hundred. Then he thought that it would be wise if he forgave his sister and moved in himself. He was seduced by their wealth and social power.

The Knowleses were originally related to the Luskins, they discovered, through a marriage generations before. When Oliver realized the connection, he felt that it was only fair to use the Luskins as his own family. He made his way in the world of business with more success using the Luskin influence. After a while, he had as little desire to acknowledge his Knowles roots as his sister. The arrangement was more than satisfactory to him.

But he did have a limit. He never wrote in the Family News. His sisters- and brothers-in-law (all seventeen of them) opened their arms, sending him the subscription and, regularly, on schedule, a reminder to submit his piece. But Oliver refused. His refusal gradually took advantage of him, for if a Luskin did not write in to the Family News, he was not officially accepted. He was forgotten.

His appearance at his sister's funeral had not, therefore, been anticipated. No one had heard any "news" of Oliver in years; he had ceased to exist, once the News itself died. And Oliver never married, a sin from the Luskin point of view. For what Oliver had come to realize, as he grew old, was that his sister had, cleverly, married into a family in which women dominated not only in numbers but also in temperament. And Oliver thought that men should rule, not women. He had managed, perhaps more successfully than he wanted, to extricate himself from the matriarchy, once he had enough money of his own.

But the Knowleses had ended with Oliver. His sister had given birth to three daughters who bore the Luskin name. Oliver had no sons named Knowles. Thus, the Luskins had proved their power to survive and to flourish. Oliver fit into no family, now. He hobbles down the aisle on his cane, like a dead stump among the varied and proliferating Luskin branches.

Barbara returns from the chapel, meeting Tom on the way out of the doors. "It's already quarter past," he says. Sadie, overhearing, takes the cue, and walks over to George. Barbara and Tom, arm in arm, turn to lead the funeral procession of married couples into the chapel. Hesitating, but urged by Sadie and George, standing near, Patrick takes Louisa's arm. The three couples, paired, stiff, disappear in the dark arc of the double-doored entry.

As they enter into the dimmed chapel the Luskins all turn their heads. The talk—whispers of Oliver's arrival, confirmations of his identity, hushes of surprise—ceases. No smiles or looks of recognition are exchanged; only hollow eyes follow the figures of the three married couples. No one knows what will happen, or if anything will happen at all. No one knows if this funeral service is merely a show of grief or a rite that will tap their hearts. The space in front of them, which the three couples approach on their way to the front pew, is empty except for a long wooden table with two oxblood ceramic vases at either end, their lipped rims open to the large window above them. They do not contain flowers.

In each mind, in the mind of Father Nathan (Mother's only surviving brother-in-law, a minister from Massachusetts); in the mind of Jewel (her heart); in the minds of Sadie's three daughters; Louisa's two sons, and Barbara's son and daughter; in the mind of Louisa's dying friend, Judith ("But I must, chérie. You will be coming to mine, soon. I

want to see how it's done."); in the minds of the confusedly
related cousins and second cousins; in the mind of Great
Aunt Carey (fuzzy); and in the minds of the three husbands
and wives is one thought in variations of memories, one
thought descending from the barren sky into the motionless
uncovered heads of the entire Luskin Family.
   —Mother is not—
   She is fleshed by

*Nathan: May she rest in peace, wherever she now lies.
Once, she looked at me, mouth curved with wit, heart obsti-
nate, and her face said, "Don't." I never knew what she meant
by "Don't" that Sunday morning I left to deliver my first
sermon.*

*Jewel: That she was always thinking was sure enough. You
could see it the way her eyebrows buckled at the tops. Her
lips, too. Sometimes I'd say, "Now, Mrs. L., don't you be
thinking till your mouth just crinkles up and goes away."
I learned not to take it as disapproval—but it took a long
time. She wasn't like most. Why, when she'd start to talking
the whole world'd shut its mouth to listen.*

*Barbara's daughter: I talked with her once. I remember,
it was about feet. I thought grandmothers never considered
feet, but she said, "You can tell a person's stature by their
feet." I wanted to hide mine under the horsehair couch, thinking how the couch itched and my feet were too large and
how I couldn't tell if grandmothers were nice or mean or
both.*

*Louisa's oldest son: She was, in her own way, imperial.
Authentic, too. Grandmother told me just last Christmas that
there were few doctors in the Luskin Family. She was glad
that I was studying to be one. Intelligence, I concluded, is
not just the result of education or opportunity. It is inherited*

just as predispositions to certain illnesses are inherited.

Maggie: At my wedding she tossed orange and white confetti from a silver tray. The wedding was at eleven-thirty. She said it was bad luck to get married in the afternoon. Then she said it was bad luck to marry. But I don't think she meant for me to hear her because she told me to run upstairs and get dressed. When I came downstairs she exclaimed, "Not wearing white?" I couldn't tell her that I wouldn't wear white because I wasn't a virgin. It was Mom's idea to have the wedding at her house. Because Grandmother couldn't make the trip across town. I married first. She didn't make it to the next wedding, whenever that will be.

Sadie: The morning of the wedding Mother took out the photographs. When she looked at the photographs from our wedding she scowled and went into the pantry. I wonder if she didn't like seeing how young she looked. Or maybe it was seeing Da. Or maybe that was me, looking at myself, thinking how young I looked—how young I was. But that one photograph we received from Maggie's wedding—tossing confetti—the spotted silk hat—the face—panic—I won't think of that now. I won't.

Louisa: Arms, arms which never embraced me. Why long for them now? They never reached out. They cut through the air to arrange the table settings, to give orders to the servants, to greet the guests. Those are her arms, wrinkled, veiny, waving through the air, Good-bye. We'll be back. Jewel and Nurse will look after you.

Barbara: Always leaving and now left. I don't want to think of journeys. I don't believe there's another journey after this one. After life. Wherever she is, she isn't. She died a week ago yesterday.

Tom: It was almost thirty years ago that I met her for the first time. My wife-to-be told me later that she had one com-

*ment. "His eyes," she had said, "are too close together." Since
then, my eyes have been too close together.*

*George: We took things from her. Gifts. Not worth much.
Their value has increased over the years, but I don't keep
track of those things the way Sadie does. I just wonder every
once in a while how one lady could have gotten so many
things in just one lifetime. One lady.*

*Patrick: I never felt comfortable with her. Especially when
Louisa and I got married. I felt I was robbing her of her
daughter. But I didn't know then that she was taking me in
—both of them, Louisa and Mother. Because when they give
something they expect it to yield a return.*

*Oliver: Never came back. Never came back. And now she's
gone first like she always did go first. Ahead of me.*

A choir of two men and two women now rise to sing. Their
conductor, a man with pink splotches covering his face, begins
the song; then stops after the first word. Irate, he turns to
The Family and announces, "Will you all now rise and sing."
Obedient, they rise and the song begins again.

There is a balm in Gilead to make the wounded whole.
There is a balm in Gilead to heal the sin-sick soul.

The soprano then takes up a verse in solo. Sadie catches the
offended expression on the woman's face as she belts out,
"If you cannot sing like angels." Sadie scowls.

The Family sits. But as soon as they have all resettled, the
choirmaster tells them to rise again. "We will now sing 'A
Mighty Fortress Is Our God.'" He waits, then turns to his
choir, which leads the Luskins in the hymn. The voices of
The Family strain with the tune; only Sadie's bold voice
can be heard striving to outsing the soprano. The song finishes
without Louisa's once opening her mouth.

As they all again sit down on the wooden pews, Louisa drops her head. Barbara and Sadie both look at her—Sadie ashamed, Barbara concerned. In the awkard silence that the choirmaster feels necessary before beginning the next song, Louisa begins to cry, trying to hide the sound of her crying in her lap. Barbara reaches out and puts her arm on Louisa's shoulder. Louisa lets it rest there, knowing that the gesture is correct in the show of grief. But Sadie quickly signals the choirmaster to begin the next song, and the senseless rising and sitting begin once more. Sadie has chosen all of the songs, with one exception. She does not know that Louisa has an arrangement with the choirmaster for the last song.

> God be in my head and in my understanding;
> God be in mine eyes and in my looking;
> God be in my mouth and in my speaking;
> God be in my heart and in my thinking;
> God be at mine end, and at my departing.

A sensible wish, Mother would have thought. To look up, sit straight. Don't forget to water the plants, close the diary. Look at each other. Can you? We all sleep, and do not ask the night what time it is.

No one has moved for a long time. The choir sits, songless. Sadie, Louisa, and Barbara, dry-eyed, look at the empty vases. They will be donated to the chapel as they are, without inscription. Empty. But they wish for streaming boughs choked into their cavities. Or a single carnation like a baby's face to remind them of beginnings, not of the end. But the vases are empty, glazed oxblood red, a glaze almost impossible to achieve. Mother made them.

The choir waits for a sign to begin the last song. Louisa

and the choir know the song; it was sung by everyone for a
long time, and the melody will be recognizable to the entire
family—though the arrangement is unusual, and will intrude,
dismantle, and confuse all who know its origin. This song
violates the Luskin Code. It was arranged by Stephen Foster
for Louisa's great-grandmother, whose daughter sang it on
the Yale Green every Sunday after church.

Louisa rises, stuffing her husband's handkerchief into his
pocket. Without taking her eyes off her sister, Sadie stands,
thinking that they will leave but suspicious that they won't.
Barbara also rises, as suspicious as Sadie. The choir rises.
The Family follows, confusion in the uneven heights of
their faces.

Louisa nods to the choirmaster. He turns to the soprano,
raising his hands on the upbeat. But with his hands still raised
she suddenly sings out

> Beautiful dreamer, wake unto me,
> Starlight and dewdrops are waiting for thee

The alto and male voices now join in

> Sounds of the rude world heard in a day,
> Lulled by the moonlight have all passed away.
> Beautiful dreamer, queen of my song

The melody rolls over in the tumbling harmonies of
Foster's arrangement as The Family holds its breath in recognition. But as the song breaks out over the air in overlap-
ping waves echoing, following, leading, rising from the depths
of the bass into the soaring descant of the soprano, as the alto
and tenor slip around each other, falling and rising, The
Family begins to hum. Louisa's lips shake. Sadie cannot resist
the melody. And then, Jewel, her heart overflowing, sings
from the far pew all the way through, her voice carrying up

into the colored waves of the rose window. Oliver taps his cane to the bounding rhythms, and now the entire family pours forth

> Beautiful dreamer, out on the sea,
> Mermaids are chanting the wild Lorelei;
> Over the streamlet vapours are born,
> Waiting to fade at the bright coming morn.

The dim light of the chapel expands to brightness. The patterns of the stained glass of the rose window distinguish their colors as The Family's voices lose their distinction and in one glowing chorus sing to the window, the soprano sending the melody out and up into the upper regions of glass. Waiting for a sign from the vibrations of light, they sing the final chorus in unison.

> Beautiful dreamer, beam on my heart,
> Even as morn on the streamlet and sea;
> Then all the chords of sorrow will part.
> Beautiful dreamer, awake unto me.

Just as the last note of the song is released, The Family holding onto it, gripping with their mouths, not willing to let it die—the light falls back into itself. The mouths of the vases rejoice in emptiness. This is what Louisa has been waiting for since Mother's death.

In a voice all can hear, Louisa turns to Patrick, and, seeming to address only him, she says, "Now, it is over." She rises, taking her coat beside her, and leaves to walk down the aisle. Patrick follows quickly. Sadie, pulling George with her, rushes past Barbara and Tom. Shaking, Barbara leans on the pew as she rises, then Tom supports her with his arm. They stumble out. Then the line of children follow; and the others make their way out in uneven lines, trying unsuccessfully to undo the moment when they sang in unison, and the song undermined the Luskin Code.

All share in Louisa's betrayal. As they bid good-bye outside, pay their respects to the chorus, kiss the sisters, shake hands with the husbands, they rush through the motions, relieved that the service is through. Families pile into cars which make their way down the twisted road of the park, disappearing down the hillside of gravestones, then rising again into view around the bend, past the flower gardens at the entrance, past the gates of the park to their separate homes.

Louisa's sons leave for Connecticut; they will be home for a late dinner. Oliver leaves behind his chauffeur without a word. Barbara's son and daughter take a taxi to the airport. Their parents will get the same flight. Sadie's daughters and son-in-law get into the car and wait.

The three couples stand at the entryway to the chapel. Sadie turns her entire body away from her husband and stands alone, facing Louisa. "What was the meaning of that song?"

In an even voice Louisa replies, "Our grandmother sang that song, with that arrangement, on the Yale Green every Sunday by popular demand. I thought it was appropriate."

"Appropriate! Appropriate! It was mad," Sadie yells. "It was madness!" George quietly moves and touches her shoulder.

"Now, dahlin'," he says in his Southern voice. "None of that."

Sadie shrugs his hand away. "None of what?" She turns to him. "I haven't done anything. I arranged all that music. Then she—she asked them to sing that crazy song without asking any of us. Barbara—Barbara did she ask you? Did she—"

"Look," Barbara says as she takes a step toward her sisters. "It doesn't make any difference now. It's been done. It's no use fighting about it now."

"I'm not fighting," Sadie says, taking a deep breath. "I just want to know if she asked you or not."

"She didn't," Barbara says, looking at Louisa. "I was just as surprised as any of us. But," Barbara says to Sadie, "I don't think that there was anything wrong."

"Yes," Tom says. "It was a beautiful arrangement."

"Beautiful arrangement? What was? The song? Or Louisa's—"

"Sadie," Louisa says, calmly. "I did not intend to hurt anyone." Deliberately Louisa leans over and kisses Sadie on her flushed cheek. The gesture immobilizes everyone for an instant.

Then Sadie bursts into tears on Louisa's shoulder. The rest shiver. Barbara, breaking off from her husband, reaches her arms around the two other women and embraces them. The husbands stand awkwardly around this trio of wives, not knowing whether to interfere.

The women's three pairs of arms—bright green, gray, and navy sleeves—crisscross in patterns around their arched female forms, rounded into one sculpture. They no longer cry, but they cannot separate themselves. Their separation from each other now will feel irreversible.

Patrick quietly interrupts the silence. "Come, Louisa. We have to leave." Louisa lifts her head, grateful. The women unwind from each other.

"Can't we all have dinner together or something?" Sadie asks.

"No, Sadie. Thank you, but we really have to go."

"And we have a plane to catch," Tom says.

"Tonight? But where—"

"Home," Barbara says. "Back to Michigan."

"But that's so far away."

"Come on, honey," George says. "Everyone's waiting."

"Oh my goodness," Sadie says. "I completely forgot." She says good-bye and rushes, embarrassed, to her family.

Louisa and Barbara stand close to each other, their husbands on either side.

"I'll call you soon."

"Okay," Louisa says, beginning to leave.

"We have to make plans about the grab."

"Oh," Louisa stops. "That's right. But let's put it off for a while, okay? I'm not really ready for it yet."

"I'll call you soon anyway—just to see how things are going." Barbara smiles, though she is thinking about what Tom told her before the service, and formulating in her mind a way to talk Louisa out of leaving Patrick. Subdued, they say good-bye. Their husbands shake hands, Patrick releasing Tom's first.

As Patrick leads his wife to their car he thinks, That song is the greatest thing I have ever seen my wife do. Sitting in the car he leans over and kisses Louisa on the lips.

Louisa stares at him after the kiss, and then, pausing, she looks away. "You told Tom, didn't you?"

"Told him what?"

"About our plans to separate."

Patrick starts the car engine, and begins to drive down the road. "You told him, didn't you?" Louisa faces him, insisting. "And you told him because you know perfectly well that if one person in The Family knows anything it is only a matter of minutes before everyone knows it and then everyone starts to exaggerate it and then—why don't you say something? Why don't you answer my question? Why did you tell Tom? Why?"

"Why did you tell Sadie that lie?"

Louisa stops. "What lie?"

"That you didn't mean to hurt anyone."

"I wasn't lying."

"Oh?" Patrick stops at the park gate. Suddenly he takes his hands off the wheel. "Louisa." He puts his arm on the seat in back of her. "This isn't the time to get into an argument. I'm sorry. I wish I hadn't said anything."

"Why did you?"

"I said, I'm sorry."

"You're avoiding my question."

He suddenly takes the wheel and accelerates. "Yes, I am. I am avoiding your question. Because I don't feel like answering it." He checks his rearview mirror. "And furthermore, I don't want to discuss anything pertaining to a divorce."

"But—"

"We just went to your mother's funeral. Isn't that enough for one day?"

Louisa reaches into her pocketbook for a cigarette. Patrick glances over.

"I wish you'd quit smoking."

"I wish you would drive home," she says, lighting it. "The boys have already left. And they drive so fast." As they leave the outer edges of Georgetown they know each other, Patrick and Louisa Morell. They know their betrayals.

A park official, who has been standing out of sight for the duration of the service, walks over to the chapel doors. Taking out a large ring of keys he locks the doors. The chapel is never used. Funny idea to have a funeral in such a rundown place.

Inside, after the doors close, the oxblood vases fall into shadow and their mouths disappear.

INVENTORIES

Barbara, sitting in her living room in Michigan, opens Sadie's letter slowly, turning the envelope, noticing the crooked type of the address and the missing "L" from Sadie's embossed initials. She slits the envelope and begins to read the two typewritten pages.

January 3, 1974

Dear Sisters,

Just one week and we begin what we've all been waiting for these past two months. And what a long two months they've been! I'm sure that both of you have put as much thought into the grab and what it means as I know I have. I've been thinking how wonderful it will be for all of us together in *her* house. I'm so happy that we've at last arranged to go through with it. I hope that both of you are as eager and excited as I know I am!

57

Barbara pauses. How can her sister continue to address everyone as if they were infants? But then, Barbara gives in to another thought: It has been a long two months, with long-distance phone calls debating what the best way to organize the grab will be. Sadie had one idea, Louisa another; Barbara felt that the decision rested with her. Two months fighting and waiting. Thanksgiving came and went. Christmas came and went. Like her sisters, Barbara could not celebrate Christmas knowing that what they were about to receive surpassed the gifts given them. And all three sisters felt the uncertainty of the objects in Mother's house—Were they gifts? Barbara continues reading:

It will be lovely to have three whole days together. Just the three of us—no husbands, no children. Naturally I understand your feelings that it would be easier for you to stay at Mother's than at my place, what with the girls all home for vacation. It's nice to have the whole family together—but three daughters and a new son-in-law! Well, you can easily imagine, after all, we were the same when we were little. I've been over to Mother's to put fresh sheets on the beds on the third floor. I'm so pleased that we will be sleeping in the same beds we had as children. Isn't that sweet? I also tidied the house a bit. For some reason—I can't for the life of me imagine why—it was left an awful mess.

So, Barbara thinks, Sadie will be staying with us. She had only expected to be there with Louisa, and, though she had misgivings, she still felt that they might have had a chance to talk about the divorce. Barbara is determined to dissuade Louisa. There has never been a divorce in the Luskin family. In all of the phone calls the past two months Louisa never mentioned it and she changed the subject when

Barbara tried to bring it up. But with Sadie there at Mother's the chance is lost. Sadie will interfere.

When I was over there getting things ready for your arrival—which is Friday, as I understand—I thought about something which I want to share with both of you. You know, in all of our talking these past months—I hate to think of our phone bills!—no one mentioned what seems to me to be the most peculiar part of the grab. I just can't understand why Mother decided that our husbands couldn't be there with us. This is really what I am writing you about.

As I was walking through the living room—just getting a sneak preview, you know—I thought to myself, Couldn't there be a way to include them—unofficially, of course. I mean, surely there are things which they would want. I know that George has a particular interest in the antique Dutch clock, the one with the ships?

So, I was thinking that it might be nice to have a preliminary grab, unofficial, which our husbands would be a part of. Through us, of course. Which made me think that there are special things that we probably want, too, and so it seemed to me that a special grab for special things, before we begin the real grab, would be the best all around.

Well, I just wanted to suggest it before we all get down there. Do write to me and tell me what you think. I'll be looking forward to your letters.

And—this is good news! Do you know that when I was having my own private preview I found an old trunk, and what do you think was inside? ALL of Mother and Da's

love letters. I wanted to read them, and I almost called up
Maggie to ask her to come over and read them with me,
when I stopped myself and realized that it would be lovely
for us to read them, all three of us, out loud to each other.
Won't that be splendid? And won't it be a joy to share
them!

I must be going now. Do think about my suggestion.
I'm sure that you will realize it makes the most sense. Particularly the part about our taking special things first—I
so want those English green and white overlay vases, the
ones in the dining room, on the left as you enter from
the living room?

See you soon soon soon—

Love, Sadie

P.S. I just realized that your letters would get here *after*
you did! How silly! Let's talk about it when you arrive.
S.C.

Clearly, Barbara thinks, the letter still in her hand, Mother
had a good reason for only allowing us to be in the grab. And
what does Sadie mean by "unofficial, of course"? There's no
such thing as an unofficial grab. Barbara sighs, knowing that
to argue with Sadie will yield nothing. The most important
thing is to fortify ourselves to get the grab done in three
days. We cannot leave anything; we must take all.

The objects—named but their inventory unread—pull, her
history pulls . . . she, who looked first upon the Flemish
Verdure tapestry, who bid highest for the Chippendale chair,
who carried the pearl inlaid tray to the sick, who rolled and
unrolled the Persian rug out of one house and into the next,

out of Virginia and into 1407 and out of 1407 and into 1331 . . . she who carried the antique round table, three-legged and with a shelf, on the seat next to her on the train from Philadelphia to Washington, who wrapped the vases in tissues, stuffing their mouths, the mirrors in newspapers, taping their frames, the silver in twine, sorting its pieces, who purchased the Chinese teakwood screen for the servants to wait behind, out of sight, who bargained for the French presentation china, a betrothal gift painted by hand on the bottom, "Offert par le Marquis de Villette à la Princesse de Lamballe," who found the Royal Worcester dessert plates knowing that the dinner plates were used in Buckingham Palace, who attended church auctions (but not the church) and then returned home to dip the chain purses in gold cleaner and find emeralds imbedded in the handles, the mesh of sixteen-karat gold, she who filled the large Capodimonte box with mint wafers, the small with butterscotches, she who had given all of these stray pieces, regal and cheap, foreign and domestic, spaces in her houses—Virginia, 1407, 1331, and countless others of varying value, from India, Paris, Virginia; from the seventeenth, eighteenth, nineteenth and twentieth centuries, she, collecting from the beginning of her life leaving them at her death—she had left them now for them to take. To receive?

The sconces stand in limbo. They tell one history, the spoils of her life in her house now jammed underneath and on top of tables jammed together, speckled with knickknacks, bordered with extra chairs perched against walls, cupboards tucked into corners, empty candy bowls, a Tiffany tobacco tin, a china orchestra of frogs accompanying the dance of the Meissen flower background figures of courtiers skirting the table tops in search of the bacchantes and cherubs on the other side, the Victorian plant stand of veneer mahogany and ormolu filled with the lace of falling ferns embroidering its legs ornately stockinged in green . . .

Barbara stops. She does not know that inventory.

Bare beige blended, her living room. Her blank picture window. Her flat-coated walls. Where? Where will Mother's —her—things go? On her Danish Modern tables? The light bumping over the layers of fabrics—she does not want that light here. It will not fit.

Barbara and Tom commissioned an architect to design this house when their combined incomes could afford it. Their married life finally arrived at the air-filled nest on on the lake, the chosen site. They intentionally designed it with little storage space. Mother's objects will intrude.

But—we married to have this house, with real light. I married Tom for . . . love? But that's not the point now. There is no sun today. The wind-wrinkled surface of the lake stirs up the clouds caught in its waves. All is tarnished by winter. What is the point now, with the sky and lake deceptively one tone, the still hanging over the moving, the moving rearing up against what is still?

After all, what is a husband? What is a husband married to a Luskin woman? He married into an old stale wealth, expecting no return; and now, as the wealth returns, he is remarried. There is no way out. Marriage looked like a way out, but now it doubles back into the lush garden, a circular path of looped petals. I can't tear off the petals to destroy the flower. The bud reblossoms; Mother dies.

When he married me he married all of the houses, he married the New York drawing room, the Virginia estate, the corner house in Georgetown, 1407, the small row house down the block, 1331, where the grab will take place. He married the Luskin journeys. He married into my parents' intermarriage, though they did not discover until after they were married that they were third cousins through another marriage. He married a line of women noted for their independence, intelligence, and exaggeration of any story which bore the name of Luskin. He married a wish that we all had to be like those women we were told we came from, those women we met at holidays, those women giving birth, investing stocks, taking pictures, writing editorials.

In most families, the woman marries into her husband's family. I wonder (Barbara continues) if there wasn't something predictable in my marriage to a man without a family. An only child. I agreed to take his name. But "Luskin" is in the middle. I still use it.

He married more than a wish to be like the original Luskin women. He married into a family where women ruled. Didn't he?

Barbara now thinks about her mother's marriage. She married, took the name Luskin, and then made it hers till she seemed to be more of a Luskin than Da. She took possession of the name, giving up her own background completely. She never considered herself a Knowles. She moved in and took over and became the queen mother.

But (Barbara thinks), What does that mean for me? For us? When we first married and now? Didn't Tom really marry me, Barbara? Not Barbara Luskin, but Barbara, the girl who always left the room first even if I did marry last?

The telephone rings.

"Hello?"

"Hello, Barbara."

"Oh, Louisa."

"Listen. Have you by any chance received a letter from Sadie?"

"I was just reading it."

"What do you think?"

"Well," Barbara looks at the letter still in her hand. "It annoyed me—"

"Annoyed you? It's awful." Louisa's voice quickens. "What is she trying to do? What does she mean by 'unofficial' and 'sneak preview'? God, sneak preview! It's disgusting. She's crazy, Barbara, crazy, talking to everybody like they're children. It's no wonder, she is such a child her—"

"Louisa, calm down."

"Well, that's why I called you instead of calling Sadie. I'm so furious I don't know what to do."

"You don't have to do anything except calm down. I do agree with you—there's something in the letter that I don't like either. But—"

"Don't like? Of course you don't like it! It's insulting. Sneak preview!"

"I know. That kind of got to me, too, but listen a minute."

"You know," Barbara hears a cigarette in Louisa's mouth. "I don't understand what she means by this idea of grabbing for our husbands, or whatever the hell she does mean. It sounds like she wants to get rid of them so that she can go ahead and get what she wants for herself."

"I didn't really think that she meant that."

"What?"

"I said I don't think that's what she meant."

"The connection's sort of bad. Can you hear me?"

"Yes, fine."

"Well, could you talk a little louder?"

"Sure."

"Not that loud."

Barbara readjusts her voice. "What I thought," she says, "was that she wished our husbands could be a part of it. Officially, I guess."

"But they are."

Barbara pauses. "Is Patrick a part of it—officially?"

"Of course."

"But—"

"Patrick is a part of it because we are still married, officially."

"You mean you're still—"

"I don't know."

There's a silence on the other end. Then, Louisa says, "Did you finally decide how we were going to do it?"

"Yes," Barbara answers. "I think that, first of all, we'll have to get it straight with Sadie that there's no such thing as a grab for special things."

"That's right. I remember that part."

"Everything's special, really," Barbara says.

"Well," Louisa takes a long drag on her cigarette. "Something might mean more to one of us than—"

"But that is something that we have to decide then, that we have to deal with as we're grabbing, not before."

"Well, that will be interesting."

"It will certainly be something."

"So, what are we going to tell Sadie?"

"Exactly what we think."

"Exactly?"

"Listen, Louisa. If we're going to get through three days in the same house together we have to begin with everything out in the open. Sadie's had two months to say what she thinks, and sending this letter when she knows perfectly well we can't write back in time is simply outrageous. We're going to do it from the beginning straightforwardly, the grab and what we say to each other."

"So, how are we going to grab?"

"You mean the procedure?"

"Yes."

"We'll draw straws or something for first choice in each room and then proceed according to age."

"That sounds straightforward enough." Again, a pause. Then, "Just one more thing, which has nothing to do with Sadie."

"Good. What is it?"

"Do you have any idea where the inventories are?"

"They've been at Mother's for all I know. Since they were made."

"But that's three years."

"Well, I never received one. Did you?"

"No, I didn't. It's funny. You'd think that Mother would have mailed them to us right away."

"She probably had some reason. They must be at 1331. They couldn't be anywhere else."

"Well, we'll find out when we get there."

"Uhmhm."

"When are you getting there, by the way?"

"Friday afternoon," Barbara says.

"You want me to pick you up?"

"Aren't you flying?"

"No. I thought I would drive down on Thursday."

"Oh. Well, don't bother. I'll take a taxi."

"Bye."

"Bye."

Louisa hangs up. Unlike the house to which Barbara and Tom moved, a house designed for their marriage, over two years ago, on a whim, Louisa and Patrick moved into a house in Connecticut much too large for their family. The height of the rooms can accommodate small trees; the floors, a waltz. The colors of the walls alternate muted peach and charged red. Turning the corner at the top of the stairs one encounters panels of blue. In her study, where she now sits, the thinly fingered light beams through the shutters, calling to her attention the problem with this house. It is not the colors, which somehow, oddly, fit together. The problem is that she can never find what she is looking for in it. Louisa always feels that she has misplaced something in her own home.

She gets up from her desk to wander, scratching a spot in the rug with her heels, then moving into the middle room with the out-of-tune piano, passing into the living room. *Where are the inventories?*

The boys aren't home, she thinks. It's funny how when the boys are home I feel married. Odd—she continues to wonder as her eyes roam through the patterned air in the rooms, the air containing the colors of her house—how there used not to be relationships. It's a word the boys taught me. When Patrick and I married there were no such things as relationships: there were two people who fell in love, got married, and raised families. It wasn't a risk, then, to have a relationship—except in terms of social rank. But now, re-lationships are a risk because—I don't know.

Louisa laughs. She remembers, suddenly, a story that a friend of hers told her when Louisa was first practicing as a psychotherapist. Occasionally she remembers the story, so that with each remembering it lodges itself into her own marriage as a theme.

There was a man, well-to-do, successful, and proud of his material accomplishments, not the least of which was his beautiful, gentle wife. She was his most dear possession. They had been married for over fifteen years without hav-ing any children. During these years they had consulted numerous doctors who informed them that they should not

or could not have children. But the man, while this dis-
couraged him, as he wished, more than anything, to provide
for a family, was strengthened by his love for his wife and
her love for him. They were considering adopting a child
when the following happened:

He was talking with a friend of his about the problem—
this friend was the husband of Louisa's friend—saying that
his marriage was beautiful, and that it was unfortunate that
two people who loved each other so much should not be able
to extend that love to a child of their own. As he was talking
to his friend, he began to hesitate, noticing his friend's
peculiar expression.

"What is it," his friend asked, "that you love so much
about your wife?"

"She's so subtle, so bright. She's not like any other woman
I've ever met. When I talk to her—and we can talk about
anything—I get the feeling that she understands me better
than any other person in the world. She nods, and her
smile—her smile more than anything else. Christ, I married
her for that smile. It's magic, it's out of another world. And
the amazing thing," the man continued, "is that it has always been this way, this complete understanding between
us. You know, I've heard about other marriages breaking
up, and I just think about how lucky I am to have such a
beautiful marriage. We would never leave each other. Never.
You know, it's almost spiritual—because of that smile."

Then his friend, placing his hand on the man's shoulder,
said quietly, "But don't you know?"

"Don't I know what?"

"You've been living with this woman for fifteen years and
no one has told you? I mean, didn't you realize that when
you first married her she—"

"She what? What are you trying to tell me?"

His friend removed his hand. "Your wife is mentally retarded."

The man, struck dumb, returned home. He told his wife what his friend had said. She nodded, her genius confirming what he told her, radiating agreement as her smile always had.

When Louisa remembers the story she always thinks, A man and a woman can live together, sleep in the same bed, exchange everything, and still not know each other. She always wonders what might have happened had the man never found out. They might have lived together happily in ignorance. But finding out, the man divorced her when the doctors confirmed his friend's statement, committed her to an institution, and remarried a bitch. In a small way, the marriage of the story resembles hers: her silence mated to his speech. But the difference was that she did speak, and in speaking they had come to know each other almost to the point of divorce. At least that is what Louisa thinks now as she walks through the house of misplaced things.

She finds that she has now wandered over to the plants in the dining room. She remembers that she watered them this morning; one is taking root. Another is only its winter stem. She walks into the pantry, glancing indifferently at the cupboards filled with china that she knows is chipped and cracked. Her glasses do not match. Moving through the back hall, as if still looking for whatever it is that she has misplaced, placed somewhere but forgotten where, she enters the kitchen, with the butcher-block table, knives loose on the surface, dulled. She does not take care of her kitchen. The stove is dirty; bricks behind it are missing. She sits down at the kitchen table, looking at the apples in the bowl. Pungent. She squishes one with her fingertip. Gathering them up she leans to dump them in the garbage can. She

closes the lid, then reproaches herself. I might have made
them into applesauce. But I never make applesauce. So why
regret the waste?

Because Mother made things all the time. And I don't.
I don't like making things.

Sadie's letter appears before her eyes, left beside the bowl
of apples earlier that morning. It is a carbon copy, just like
the letters Mother would send them when they were away
at boarding school.

Sadie's sneak preview has been a week-long inspection of
the entire house. Telling her family that "there's just so
much to get ready for the grab," she has spent the days at
Mother's and the nights at home, a suburb only fifteen minutes away. She and George have lived near to Mother their
entire married life, and never considered moving. The only
way that Sadie will move now is internally, planning to redo
the entire interior of her house with Mother's things. She
has counted and recounted sets of silverware and china,
opened and reopened drawers, unbolted cupboards with a
set of keys lying on the table in the downstairs hallway,
inviting her to open the closet doors and sealed desk tops.
She has gone over everything on the first floor, startled to
find that Mother had more things than even her days of
entertaining could have found use for. Imported and inherited, they reflect off their chiseled crystal surfaces the
first New York drawing room in the early part of the
nineteenth century to the last Family Thanksgiving luncheon, five years ago. Counting only eleven dining room
chairs, Sadie went in search of the missing twelfth, a search
that took her up the stairs to the second floor and into its
rooms.

This house, the third in her Mother's marriage, is constructed entirely of hallways, diminishing in width and length as one ascends the staircase. The second floor has fewer rooms than the first, the third fewer than the second. One moves from the rooms that adults populated to rooms that children stayed in, from real dinner parties to the pretend parties of dolls. As she passed in and out of the rooms she refused to enter her mother's bedroom. She found the chair in the upstairs study, its seat covered with quilt scraps sewn together by hand. She brought the chair downstairs and placed it against the wall in the dining room. She sat down, then suddenly, without knowing why or where she was going, she went back up the stairs and into her mother's bedroom. Before she knew what was in her hands she had left the room with three red folders, labeled, "Inventory 1331 N Street: May–June 1970." She did not see the room when she entered or when she left. The day that she took the inventories was the day that she wrote to her sisters.

Now, the day that her sisters received her letter, she rushes into her own front hall. "Girls! Girls! I'm home!" No answer.

Well, Sadie takes off her gloves and enters the living room. An uninteresting room, filled with odd bits and pieces of things her daughters have made, from kindergarten through college. She glances around, the lists of the inventory in her head. Oh, she thinks, I can't wait to redo the entire thing! Properly. The green velvet couch will look perfect right there, and the two Queen Anne chairs—why, they can go into the corner there, in front of the French doors. And I really do need new curtains. George mentioned how much he was getting tired of the ones we have—didn't he? Yes, he did. I'm sure he did. So won't Mother's be a lovely addition! I'll have to measure to make sure that they fit. But I can always have them altered.

Sadie has not read through the entire inventory. She has only had time to read the dining room and living room, exhausted by the lists, and exhausted by the constant comparison of her house to Mother's, a contest in which Mother's always wins. She used to like her house, particularly the living room. But now she hates it; loves the dream room she envisions after the grab is over.

She has stopped rushing back and forth to concentrate on the things listed in the inventory. She has asked George the value of certain pieces, and George, uninterested, has quoted some interesting figures to her nonetheless. Why, the silver! Some of it is worth thousands! And the sconces—who knows what they're worth? And the Virginia Sheraton pieces? Those will look lovely.

The front door opens. Her second daughter Maggie and her son-in-law of less than a year enter.

"Oh," Sadie says, turning, her hands flying up to her face. "I can't wait!"

Maggie looks at her mother. "For what?"

"The grab! The grab! Just think of it, Maggie, just think of it. Think how beautiful our house will be!"

"Mom," Maggie begins, then stops. Maggie is thinking of the apartment that she and Mark have just looked at, unfurnished. But then it occurs to her that the kind of furniture her mother will be grabbing cannot be put into their apartment. She has lived with her mother's taste for twenty-two years and knows that the furniture shouldn't go in this house either; but is resigned that it will.

"Yes, Maggie? What is it?"

"Oh, nothing. Except that we just found an apartment and we'll be moving out by the end of the month."

"Can you afford it?"

"Yes, we can," Mark says. He has wanted to leave his in-laws since he was fired from his job.

"That's wonderful," Sadie says. "You both must be so excited."

"Yes," Maggie says.

"Is it furnished?"

"No," Mark says, "it isn't, Mrs. Caldwell."

"Well, what are you going to do?"

"We were thinking of—"

"We'll figure out something," Maggie interrupts her husband. "Come on," she takes Mark's hand. "Let's make something to eat."

"I was just going to make dinner for all of us," Sadie says.

"Oh," Maggie turns to Mark. "Would you like to go out?" Mark, still uncomfortable in this house, shrugs his shoulders.

"We have plenty here," Sadie says.

"We'll go out," Maggie says, and leaves.

"Bye, Mrs. Caldwell," Mark says.

"You can call me Sadie by now." She smiles.

"I'm kind of used to Mrs. Caldwell," he says, following his wife.

And the vases, Sadie thinks, going into the kitchen. They'll look gorgeous on the living room mantel.

The inventories of this story are now complete. Maggie and Mark have left their mother's house, and will not return. Sadie, Barbara and Louisa enter their mother's house, for they are the last of the Luskin line to grab at their mother's marriage to furnish their own.

❧ FIRST FLOOR ❧

TAGGING

LATE THURSDAY NIGHT LOUISA ENTERS HER MOTHER'S HOUSE silently. As she opens the door, the street light throws the frame of the hallway mirror into grotesque shadow figures. Quickly Louisa shuts out the light. Then she moves through the hallway, darkly, to the lamp on the table below her mother's portrait. Bumping into the shade her fingers fumble for the switch. Her mother's figure lights up from below. Someone is walking upstairs. She looks up. She turns. A figure stands at the top of the stairs in a white nightgown.

"Who's there?"

"Sadie?" Louisa says.

"Oh my god! Looza!" Sadie rushes down the stairs, her nightgown skirting the edges of the stairs. "Jesus, you scared me."

"I scared *you*!"

"But how did you get in?" The sisters kiss each other.

"I had a key."

"But how could you have a key?"

"What are you doing here?" Louisa stands with her back to the painting of Mother.

"I thought you weren't coming until tomorrow."

"Oh—I'm sorry. But it's lucky that I did come tonight. It's snowing."

"Is it?"

"Yes, a lot."

"Here," Sadie goes to get Louisa's bags by the front door. "You must be exhausted."

"I'm more cold than tired," Louisa says. Sadie puts the bags on the bottom of the stairs. "What time is it, anyway?"

"I have no idea. It's past midnight, though."

"Let's have some cocoa in the kitchen, okay?" Sadie smiles.

"Scotch, then cocoa—maybe," Louisa says, following the large white figure of her sister through the narrow hall.

"Suit yourself," Sadie says.

Hours later the light beneath Mother's portrait goes out. Outside it snows continuously; a snowstorm beginning in the Northwest, hitting Michigan two days before Barbara left for Washington, traveling ahead of her plane south and east. The skies do not indicate the time of her arrival (delayed) but hide the hours behind their whitely downfalling density.

Snow in Washington estranges the landscape, viewed through the frame of her cab window. Summer is Washington, the heat of their weddings; not this blank cold, merging white on white, the columns of monuments rising pale into the air, interrupting its sheath of winter.

Barbara arrives at her mother's street, the row houses indistinguishable from each other, all of them whitened by the snow. The sticky flakes sizzle, muted, through the space between Barbara and her mother's house. She stands outside, looking. Layers of white fall unevenly as the flakes fall one upon the other into irregular shapes on the ground. The steep steps glisten, absorbing the white at contact, warmer here in the tightly packed street than the waste of the runway. A slight change of temperature. Barbara stares at the house: three tiers of windows she follows up to the top as the flakes drop into her eyes, off-white sets of blinds striped horizontal against the vertical path of the snow. The house absorbs her, will absorb her when she walks up the stairs and into the hall as she will in a moment—Why pause? I am late. I should be in a hurry to start. Sadie and Louisa will be worried and waiting. They must be sitting in the living room; its light glows old yellow in the window, decorated by the green-shadowed black ferns in the plant stand. It is night at noon and noon at night and not yet time to start. The snow grace-lessly tumbles over the wrought-iron railings. The branches of the ivy bordering the steps pop out of the network of leaves like dislocated bones, and still Barbara cannot enter.

She is convinced that this house is the wrong house. She did not expect to arrive here, at 1331. She expected to enter the doors of 1407, the house around the corner and across from the church. Not 1331, but 1407. 1407, from which Sadie first married, Louisa second, and Barbara last, on impulse. The other house, rambling over half a block, with a garden and a greenhouse. Not this upright box in front of her, but the spread of clapboards. Not these stairs, but the spiral stair-case. Not these blinds, but the curtains. Not these French doors, but the solid oak. Not

"Barbara!" Sadie opens the door. "You'll catch your death of cold!" Barbara shivers, the cold finding its places on her body. Carefully, carrying her suitcase, she ascends the stairs,

Sadie rushing to meet her halfway and take her suitcase from her. Pushing Barbara into the house, she says, "Quick, there's a fire in the living room. Yes, yes, Louisa's here. She's been here since last night. She drove down just ahead of the storm. We've been having a lovely time together—lovely! Just imagine!"

Barbara walks into the living room. In front of the fire Louisa sits crossing her thin legs in a rust wool pantsuit. The ski pants and sweater cling to Barbara's body. She sits, then Louisa rises and offers her the chair closet to the fire. "Here," she says. "It's the warmest."

"Thank you," Barbara says, as Louisa kisses her hello.

"Would you like something to drink?"

"Yes, I would," Barbara says, removing her boots which have stained the rug. "Some coffee would be great."

"I'll get it."

"Thank you." Barbara looks around her, her eyes moving from the rug up to the ashtrays littered with filters to the walls and finally her eyes drift out to the hall mirror, which reflects the wall on the other side. Her eyes return to the living room. It looks basically untouched. Sadie must have . . . Remembering the letter, Barbara wonders if Louisa has mentioned anything to Sadie yet. Probably not.

A cup of coffee appears at her side. She looks up, expecting to see Louisa. Sadie smiles back.

"Oh," Barbara says.

Sadie sits down next to her. "Oh, Barbara, you don't have to worry about anything."

"What do you mean?"

"I mean the stuff I wrote in that letter." Expecting Sadie to continue, Barbara waits; but nothing follows.

"Well," she says, her hair now beginning to lift from her

temples, "that's good. I didn't think it was a good idea."

"Oh, it was unnecessary," Sadie says. "Where's Looza?"

"I don't know."

Then Barbara notices that Sadie is wearing a ruby-studded brooch on her blouse. The brooch belonged to Mother, pinned daily to her collars. On Sadie the jewel is a mistake; it hangs heavily off the frills. About to ask why she wears it, Barbara stops, remembering the division of the jewelry almost exactly a year earlier. Mother was the overseer of their selections, briefly commenting on each one. There will be none of her comments now, dividing up her house.

Louisa enters, shaking her head. "Well," she says, "I give up. I can't find them anywhere." She sits down and lights a cigarette.

"Can't find what?"

"Oh, Looza's been positively obsessed with the inventories," Sadie explains. "She got up this morning and she's been looking for them since. She can't find them anywhere. I keep on telling her that it doesn't really make any difference because here we all are and here is everything of Mother's and that seems to be all that's necessary for the grab, but she insists that the inventories are necessary and so it's been going back and forth like that since she arrived."

"And you can't find them?"

"I've been through the whole house," Louisa says, "and they just aren't here."

"That's strange," Barbara says. "But Sadie does have a point." Barbara again scans the room. "I don't think that the inventories are necessary; but I do think they would make it easier." Barbara gets up. "I'll look," she says.

"It isn't necessary," Louisa says. "I've been through the whole place, and I can't find them."

"Did you look in Mother's room?"

"Yes, that was the first place I did look. And they weren't there."

"I helped Looza," Sadie says. "And, really, Barb, I'm sure that they aren't anywhere we've looked."

Barbara sits back down. "Well, I guess we can start without them. They might show up."

"But the inventories should be here," Louisa says.

"But the fact is they aren't."

"Oh, Looza, it would be more fun without them, don't you think?" Louisa makes no reply.

"Well, let's begin." Barbara takes a package of pipe cleaners from her pocketbook and folds three of them into different lengths. Then, setting them aside, she takes out three rolls of tape—bright blue, red and yellow. "Sadie, what color would you like?"

"Oh, I really would like the blue. Blue is my favorite color. Always has been." Sadie takes the roll.

"Louisa?"

"I guess I'll take the red," Louisa says.

"That leaves me the yellow, which is fine. Now," Barbara says, her voice smoothing as she talks, "as you both know the procedure is simple and to the point: We draw these pipe cleaners for the first choice in each of the rooms. Whoever gets the longest pipe cleaner gets first choice. Then we take turns according to age, so that if Louisa gets first choice, I would get second and Sadie, you would get third. Okay?" Barbara puts the pipe cleaners in her fist, with her back turned, and extends her fist to Sadie. Sadie takes one, then Louisa, then Barbara opens her hands. First choice falls to Sadie.

She stands up, quickly. "Oh, I'm first. How do I do it? I mean, what should I start with?"

"You simply start with what you want," Barbara says. Sadie's roll of tape rotates around her thumb, a spinning disc of blue. Her eyes take in the entire living room in one calculated swing of her head. She knows the contents of the room thoroughly. Her eyes stop at the green velvet settee. Silently she walks over to it and, ripping off a large piece of tape, she sticks it to the arm of the settee.

"There," she stands back.

"I wouldn't use that much tape if I were you," Barbara says. "I've only got five rolls for each of us."

"Now whose turn is it?" Sadie swirls to face them, her body smiling.

"Louisa's," Barbara says. Louisa rises. She takes her turn by walking to the center of the living room and placing a small but conspicuous rectangle of red in the middle of the Persian rug. Then Barbara quietly steps over and a strip of yellow falls across one of the one thousand and one Buddhas' plump laps. They continue, gradually marking the living room with red, yellow and blue squares, rectangles and stripes, transforming the room from a residence into an antique shop, the colors of their choices like the color codes of prices or of periods. The transformation from a home to a bidding place works in the sisters: they move from object to object like well-trained antique buyers, as their mother must have moved through the auctions every Wednesday, politely choosing, reservedly tagging, bargaining with themselves individually. For each carved figurine there is another; for one table, another; for one couch, a lounge; for one box, a jar. They move through the room without comment, a cappella, their movements orchestrated by their expressions—Barbara's straight lips, Louisa's blank pupils, Sadie's quivering cheeks. In a dance following the pattern of the Persian rug, as intricate as the threads of its colors, Barbara steps in stockinged feet around the chairs. Louisa maneuvers in small steps through the tables and wooden desks. Sadie flutters like a ballerina around the small Staffordshire bacchantes and cherubs, ranking them with blue. The daughters lean and stretch, bend and rise with the figures on the tapestry caught in the cloth as the daughters are caught in the room, interweaving their bodies slowly to reveal their individual patterns as more of the things in the room change from her hands to theirs. Barbara leans to the foreign objects, particularly from India; Louisa reaches out for the memories; Sadie pirouettes through the ornate and precious. But these patterns are only part of the general pattern of their motions, for each of the sisters deliberately chooses to ignore the choices of the other two to coordinate their dance without expressing surprise, disappointment, relief. The dance continues to wind, circle, unwind, encircle, as the female trio, unpartnered by husbands, unaccompanied by inventories, moves through the room with the reserve and courtesy of a sixteenth-century pavane.

Then, abruptly, the pavane is broken. Sadie moves over to the plant stand, centered between two shelves on each wall of china frogs, an orchestra called the Frog Band. She tags the shelf on which each section of this orchestra stands, underlining them with blue. This odd little band of Staffordshire china belonged to Barbara and Da, who used to talk to real frogs when they sat beside the lake together the summers Barbara was a child. They would pretend that the orchestra played for them alone; he used to tell Barbara stories about the Frog Band until an entire drama about the violinist and the cellist against the conductor and the drummer grew up between them as Barbara grew up with them. Barbara assumed that neither of her sisters would even consider taking the Frog Band, dressed in green jackets and wobbling on their spindly legs. They did not know their stories.

Sadie stands in front of the Frog Band for a moment, then, turning, she says, "They are so adorable! I can't wait to have grandchildren!"

"But—" Louisa begins, looking at Barbara. Barbara quickly looks away. "Barbara?"

"Yes? what?" But she does not face Louisa.

"I'm afraid I'm a little confused," Louisa says.

"Why, Looza?"

"Well," Louisa tries, "Well, I just thought that—that the Frog Band belonged to Barbara."

"Don't be silly," Barbara says, now turning to face her sisters. "The Frog Band belongs to Sadie."

"But—"

"Looza, I just tagged it, see? I've always loved them!"

"But, Sadie, don't you think—"

"Louisa, this is not necessary," Barbara says.

"What is going on? Now I'm confused," Sadie says.

"Nothing, Sadie. I have no idea what Louisa is so confused about." Quickly Barbara looks around the room. "Well," she says, "it looks as if we've pretty much finished in here. Let's move out to the hall."

Sadie rushes out the living room doors. Louisa pauses, then she says, quietly, "Barbara, why didn't you say something?"

"Because there was nothing to say."

"But Sadie shouldn't have—"

"It was Sadie's turn, Louisa. I do not wish to discuss it." Barbara rises to go out to the hall.

"Okay," Louisa says, "if that's the way you feel. But—but the Frog Band meant something to you, didn't it? It doesn't mean anything to Sadie."

"You don't know that," Barbara says.

"You were the one who said that we should try to be honest with each other. At least, that's what I remember you said."

"I am being honest."

"I guess we have different ideas of honesty," Louisa says, gently, wondering why Barbara, who insists on being open, should have been closed, didn't demand what was hers. She makes one last effort. "Do you want to know what I think?"

"No." Barbara walks past the frogs and out into the hall, which is lit through the glass doors by the reflection of the snow. Barbara looks at the sweating glass, trying to force the snow over her memory of summer beside the lake. She hears Louisa leave the room; the strike of a match; and then Barbara turns to see her two sisters standing in front of the portrait.

"I don't know what we're going to do about it," Sadie says.

"What do you mean *do* about it?" Barbara says, approaching them.

"I mean, how are we going to grab it?"

"We can't," Louisa says.

"That's what I mean: We can't, so what are we going to do?"

"Nothing. There's nothing to be done."

Louisa turns her eyes from the portrait to Sadie and then back to the portrait, as if considering a problem objectively. Then, her expression so unlike the expression of the woman on the wall, painted, that she looks less like a daughter than a visitor to the house, she says, "I think that Mother meant to give the portrait to one of us before she died."

"Fine," Barbara says. "Except that she's dead and the portrait is here."

"I think," Louisa continues, "that Mother did make some decision before she died. I'm certain of it. But she never told—" The air flutters around her sisters. "Did she—"

"She never said anything to me," Sadie says, disappointed.

"Nor to me."

"Well. She probably wrote it down somewhere," Louisa recovers the air into her words, "and we will find out where."

"Probably in the inventories," Barbara says.

Probably in the diary, Louisa thinks. Why didn't I look in it when I found it? Because I don't really want to find out? Is that why I hid it in my room and didn't read it?

"No, she didn't," Sadie says. She looks up, her eyes suddenly recording her mistake. "Oh, dear, I didn't mean to— I—"

"Sadie," Barbara says.

"I know. I know," Sadie looks away.

"Obviously you do know."

Sadie stands still, facing the portrait. "I don't know what got into me," she says, trying to smile. "I mean, I really did think that it would be more fun if we did try to do it without the inventories and I really did think that they weren't necessary because they aren't, not for the grab. They're necessary, but not for this—I mean, we did do it, didn't we? How silly of me! I don't know what made me do that. I'm sorry. It's not like I stole them or anything. I was just thinking—just this moment I was thinking that I would go and get them because it is kind of tiring to try to grab with just our eyes, and I think we probably can't help overlooking things, because Mother stuffed things in so many places, and so I think I'll go and get them right now because here we are in front of her portrait and maybe she's written it there and I just didn't see it or something and I want to know what she did decide, if she decided anything, and anyway, we would have found the inventories soon because they're right there"— Sadie points—"in that drawer, and I thought it would be nice to find them, you know, all three of us because I have read them but not completely, and because I didn't really think that they were that important for the grab."

"I don't understand why you didn't just give them to us in the beginning," Barbara says.

"I told you, Barbara, I thought it would be more—"

"That's not the point. The point is that you lied."

"I didn't lie. I never said that I didn't know where they were. I just said that it would be more fun without them."

"Where are they?"

"Here," Sadie rushes down the hall and takes out the red folders from the desk on which the telephone sits, not yet disconnected.

"Now," she smiles, "this one is Louisa's, because—see?— Mother had them initialed. And this is yours, and let's see," Sadie opens up hers, "yes, this is mine." A slip of paper falls out. Sadie picks it up.

"What's that?" Louisa says.

"This? Oh, it's just a list that George gave me." Sadie puts it back into her copy of the inventory carefully. Then she looks up and suggests they get something to eat.

The inventories, aside from their interest, also reveal to the daughters that despite appearances a few of the objects in the living room have not yet been tagged. After their snack, they return to finish what they overlooked, and then they move into the front hall. They do not have to depend on their eyes, but now rely on the words and the comments in front of them. The silence of the first effort gives into voices as the daughters mutually discover, Sadie as much as Louisa and Barbara, details about the histories of the objects in their mother's house; and this education carries them through the front hall, from the mirror to the horsehair couch back to the center of the first floor. They reach the portrait, guided now by the order of the inventory superimposed upon the order of the furniture. They choose from the various things on the table when the portrait stops them again.

"It isn't in here," Sadie says.

"I know," Barbara says. "I noticed that before in the kitchen."

"Why didn't you mention it?"

"Because I didn't think it would be important. I assumed you would have noticed the omission. It's rather conspicuous."

"Well, what are we going to do now?" Sadie says. "What does it mean?"

"It means, simply," Louisa says, "that Mother indicated somewhere else what her decision was."

"But where?"

"I don't know."

"Louisa," Barbara asks, suspicious, "when you were looking for the inventories, did you find anything else that might have—?"

"No. No, I didn't," Louisa answers, a little too quickly. "Not even in Mother's room. There wasn't anything but her copy of Hopkins, the Montaigne, you know, and some of her other books." But when I saw the diary, Louisa thinks, I knew exactly what it was. I didn't think about the portrait. I don't even care about the portrait. But the diary—that's Mother as I never knew her.

"Well," Barbara says, "we'll have to find out eventually. We have to go through everything in the entire house, and if she did decide, as she must have, we'll know by the end of the weekend."

"Yes," Sadie says, "we must go through absolutely everything. I can't believe it, but we do."

"Well," Louisa begins.

"Well, what?"

"Well—nothing."

Barbara, turning the page of the inventory, sees the heading DINING ROOM.

"We really should go into the dining room," she says.

"Do we have to draw straws again?" Sadie asks.

"Yes."

On the way, Barbara turns on the light beneath the portrait.

TRADING

Suddenly, the cordially turning, openly presented faces, the extended arms are replaced with oblique shoulders, diverted eyes, and the syncopation of greed. Sadie leads their dance in a flutter, a frantic pace, as the night encloses the daughters within the walls of their mother's house. The lights are all turned on, a gesture in deference to the night outside; but time, the continuous black snow, falling, is forgotten.

The lights startle Louisa. Sadie glides about the showroom, pressing Barbara to make the pipe cleaners ready for the grab in the dining room. But Barbara, stretching to touch the floor, continues her exercise. Louisa fortifies herself with a cigarette, and peruses the inventory.

"Come on, Barb," Sadie says, standing next to her.

"Just a minute; I'm trying to wake myself up."

"Wake yourself up? You're tired? I'm wide awake! How about you, Looza, are you tired?"

91

"I'm fine," Louisa says. "Except for almost running out of cigarettes." Louisa is, however, exhausted; not by the hours spent alternating between taking and losing; but from taking one thing and saying nothing about it. She finds herself in the too-familiar position of being the one who will probably know first. *Sadie never knows anything—anything naturally. Barbara comes to know things slowly, and with too much coaxing. My place is to know and to hate knowing—*

Barbara again holds out the prepared fist. The sisters draw. First choice falls to Barbara. Taking her copy of the inventory in her hands she walks through the dining room only slightly refreshed, beginning to be bored by the endless lists of objects, and the decisions that run in circles through them. Barbara begins to check the things in the room with the written list in her hands, appearing preoccupied with the Virginia Sheraton chairs.

"What's taking so long?" Sadie asks.

"Just a minute," Barbara says, walking around the dining room table counting the chairs one by one. Then she sees the extra chair against the wall. Without turning to face Sadie, stationed at the other side of the table, she says, "Mother has eleven chairs listed here. But there are twelve in the room. The inventory expressly states that the twelfth chair is upstairs. Sadie, how do you account for the chair against the wall?"

"Oh, Barbara," Louisa interrupts, "don't be so petty. What's one chair, for Chrissake?"

"Not upstairs."

"Oh," Sadie says. "I brought it downstairs when I was checking out the house."

"The sneak preview?"

"Yes."

"More of a sneak than a preview."

"Barbara, this is ridiculous," Louisa says.

"Oh, so you've changed your mind. You were just as worried about this as I was—more worried, if I remember correctly. Furious, as I recall."

"What do you mean?"

"I mean," Barbara says, "a worried phone call about a week ago."

"Oh, that."

"What are you two talking about?"

"Sadie, I thought, or I was under the impression, that you had been here only to prepare for our arrival, not to move Mother's things. Apparently, you did more than to take the inventories, which was bad enough, but —"

"Don't talk to me as if I were a child, Barbara. I'm not, you know."

"Well, if you're not a child then why do you do things so childishly? Why did you move this chair?"

"Because I had some practical sense and thought that it would be easier if it were down here since it does belong to the set and there seemed to be no point in leaving it upstairs."

"Practicality isn't the point," Barbara says.

"I know," Sadie says. "I know what you're thinking. You think that I shifted everything around, don't you? Especially since I did take the inventories, for which I apologize. But you seem to forget that I am just as concerned that Mother's things stay in order as much as you are. I don't understand why I did what I did with the inventories, but that's something else. The point is that we can't fight. That's the point."

"I agree," Louisa says.

"I agree also," Barbara says. "Which is why I'm bringing the issue up. Look, let's get it over with now. Sadie, is there anything else in the house that your practical sense has made you move around?"

"No. Mother kept everything in order, absolutely everything except this silly chair, which she probably took up there so that Da could have visitors. Don't you think that's why?"

"Probably," Barbara says, reminded of the visits to the study which doubled as Da's convalescence room. "I wish," Barbara says, then stops.

"Wish what, Barb?" Sadie moves slowly closer to her sister.

"Wish that these things were just things and not complicated by moving around and bringing on memories. But that's not the important thing now. Let's quit this," Barbara says. Sadie moves over to kiss her, when Louisa interrupts.

"You were the one who started it."

"Started what?"

"Fighting."

"And you're the one who is starting it all over again."

"No, I'm just making my own point about this—that you began an unnecessary argument over nothing."

"Nothing? I suppose you feel that the things in this house are just like anything you might buy in some fancy store?"

"No, I feel just the opposite: that I could never buy these things in a fancy store."

"Not because you couldn't afford it."

"No. Because they wouldn't be for sale."

"Of course they would."

"Forget it, you don't understand what I'm trying to say."

"And what don't I understand?" Barbara says, her fingers scrambling at her hair.

"I understand," Sadie says quietly.

"Well, do tell us," Barbara says.

"Please, Barb, don't be like that," Sadie says. Barbara's hands fall to her sides as Louisa's hand falls down slowly with the smoke of her cigarette trailing in an arc. "You're

both right, of course, because the things here are special and
at the same time they are just things, things which Mother
bought once. They are things which are Mother's and now
they're just things which we own. So it's like they're special
and then not special."

"You're not making any sense," Barbara says.

"Oh, but I am making sense, really. You see, when I did
read some of the inventory, I found out that it wasn't the
same as the things in the house. Which is why I stopped reading it. I didn't want to read the inventory. I wanted to see
the things. And so then it struck me how the things were
special when I saw them, but they weren't special when I
only read them and I couldn't really see them and imagine
that Mother was—"

"Oh God," Louisa says. "Don't you ever stop talking?"

Sadie's eyes crisp into cold blue. Louisa looks up and is
hit by them. "I'm sorry," Louisa says, quickly putting the
end of her cigarette to her lips to forbid any more words
from coming out of her mouth.

"Sorry? But Looza, I'm the one who should be sorry," Sadie
says. "It's all my fault. I was the one who moved the chair."

"No, no," Barbara says, "I'm the one who should apologize.
Louisa's right: I brought us to this point. I am sorry."

"We're all overdoing it," Louisa says.

"Agreed. So let's stop. Now, whose turn was it?"

"Yours." Sadie laughs. "It's your turn."

"Well," Barbara says, "now that I've made such a big pro-
duction out of them, I'll take them."

"The chairs?" Sadie says.

"Yes," Barbara begins systematically to tag each one of
them, the one against the wall first. Sadie's eyes follow Barbara around the dining room table; Louisa's eyes follow
Sadie's. Suddenly, Louisa laughs.

"What are you laughing at?" Sadie turns to her, but not completely.

"You."

"Me?"

"Yes. I'm laughing because it just occurred to me there was another reason that you moved the chairs." Barbara tags the last one.

"Yes, I did move them for another reason."

"Sadie."

"Oh, Barbara, it's nothing. I just wanted them, that's all."

"Well, you just lost them," Barbara says. "Louisa, it's your turn."

"Wait," Sadie says, her body jumping with an idea. "Barb?"

"What now?"

"There's no rule about trading, is there?"

"Trading?" Louisa says, interested. Barbara stands with her hands resting on the back of a chair.

"I'll make a deal with you, Barbara."

"A deal?"

"Yes, yes," Sadie begins with a sigh, which accelerates into breathing notes. "If we can trade things . . . I just love these chairs so much and I wanted them especially, because I was thinking just a little while ago how sick I am of the set I have, and—and, well, I'd just love to have them so much. They're so delicate. And they're from the South, or almost the South, which of course is important to George. So they are in another way special to me, and they mean so much," the daughter who has scrupulously chosen the objects of the highest monetary values continues, "but," she draws out, "but although it is difficult, extremely difficult for me, I'd be willing to sacrifice—and it would be a sacrifice, a great sacrifice, because I love them so much, but I would, I really would be willing to trade the chairs for the adorable frogs, you know, the Frog Band?" Sadie continues, "The Frog Band, as you know, meant a great deal to me as a little girl, and I cherish them, I really cherish them, but these chairs—well, I really need them. It's an awful sacrifice to make, but I would be willing to trade with you, Barbara, that is, if you want the Frog Band. It isn't worth much, except, you know, as a reminder of our childhood together."

Barbara stands rooted to the chair. No amount of exercise would loosen the tension in her limbs, affixed to the chair. *Isn't worth much except as a reminder of whose childhood, hers or mine? If only these objects didn't interfere. If only this were an auction.* Barbara's entire body now strains against the house absorbing her, from her feet planted firmly up through her muscled thighs and into her arms tensely gripping at the chair and then exploding in her head. *We're fighting. The fact is I'm losing control of the situation.* Barbara stands looking at the objects, wishing she could convince herself that they were things that anyone could buy in a store. *Why do the Luskins have this tradition? Nobody else does. What is the point? Love?* They are all confronted with what Barbara now confronts; though she wants more than the others to resist, hating the memories inside the objects, hating losing, hating how they make her think about herself and her sisters and reminding her why she always wanted to leave the room first. Inside Barbara tries to persuade herself *These are just things. Things things things. They aren't anything but things. Oh God women are the stupidest creatures. We're so goddamned materialistic and petty.* She generalizes safely, unable to word the words of her feelings, the word *we,* the word *us,* the word *her.*

"Barbara?" Louisa asks. "Are you all—

"Of course I'm all right."

"So you've agreed?" Sadie asks.

"No, I haven't agreed. I didn't say that." Sadie drops her hands helplessly to her sides; they bounce and land beside her hips.

"Why?"

"Because I don't want to," Barbara says, stiff.

"But we can," Louisa says, "trade—as a matter of procedure."

"Certainly. It's a good idea." Barbara now picks up the inventory left on the dining room table. "Now, whose turn is it?"

"Is it mine or yours?" Louisa asks Sadie.

"I think it's yours."

"Well, Sadie, before I take my turn, I'd like to ask you if you want the chandelier."

"What are you asking me for?"

"I'm just curious."

"I do, as a matter of fact. But it's your turn, so you take it if you want it."

"Listen, we can't negotiate this way," Barbara says. "It takes too much time."

"Oh, I don't really think that it will, Barbara," Louisa says, rising and tagging a drop of glass with red. Sadie then goes directly over to the English green and white overlay vases on the mantel, marking each with a small square of blue. These vases were filled and emptied with flowers by Mother and Louisa. Louisa would take out the flowers that Mother put in fresh each morning.

"Sadie," Louisa says, "I'll trade you the chandelier for the vases."

"It's a deal," Sadie says, smiling.

The division of the dining room continues without interruptions. For lack of space in the living room many objects one would not expect to find in a dining room have been tucked into corners. The inventory is now indispensable to finding all of the things. Before, in the living room, they had all been controlled by the necessity to see. But now that tension is gone. The inventory sustains them, and events, what they have said to each other and found out about each other, have changed the way they move through Mother's rooms. The taut strings suspending rivalry are now completely slack, and drag along the floor over the weave of the rugs, the threads that bound them together in a fight to grab what each saw first are free now, as they move independent of each other, holding their private, initialed copies of the inventory against their bodies when they pull off their strips of tape. Each daughter is screened from the other by her mother's master list, taking turns.

Barbara: Women may be pitifully emotional, but I'll be damned if I lose again because of my feelings. The thing is to play by the rules, even if we are making up the rules as we go along. Even if one of those rules is that I am reminded of her every time I rip off another strip of yellow tape. The grab is just a family tradition, part of the Code. Luskins are supposed to grab. And it's a waste of time to let these feelings—one sister stealing, the other giving opinions I don't want to hear and don't understand—get in the way of what we have to do.

Louisa: Every time I take one thing, I feel something is missing. The strain of being here with them forces this empty feeling up to the surface. It's so hard to say what we really want. Because as soon as we admit that we want something it's gone. So I pretend, I hide what I really want, what I have upstairs, from myself and from them. The diary should be missing from this house. It should have been

*burned when she was burned. So that I wouldn't have
stolen it.*

*Sadie: I wish we weren't fighting. Oh God I wish Barbara
and Louisa weren't fighting. Why didn't Barbara trade with
me? Mother left us so many beautiful things. Certainly
enough for everyone. So why does it feel like there's not
enough? I never thought that Mother had so many things.
They must have been much richer than they ever let on.
It's like there are too many things and aren't enough things.
But I know Mother: She wants us to take everything and
be happy that they were so rich and fill ourselves up with
what she left. And she doesn't like fighting. She never fought
with anyone, ever.*

"I'm tired," Sadie says as Louisa tags the Chinese teakwood
screen that Jewel used to tease Mother about. ("Why, Mrs.
L., you always be hiding someone behind it.")

"What time is it?" Barbara asks, yawning from the corner.

"I'll go and see," Sadie says. She is not interested in the
time, however. She has an odd feeling that the Dutch clock
in the hall has been taken from her while she has been in
the dining room.

The clock hands read a few minutes past three o'clock.
For a moment Sadie thinks that it tells the correct time. But
then she notices that the clock isn't ticking. "Of course," she
murmurs, "no one has wound it." Seeing the blue spin-
naker of tape across the bow of a small ship, she is relieved. She rushes back to the dining room where only
Barbara sits.

"Where's Looza?"

At the same time that Barbara says, "In the living room,"
Louisa calls to Sadie.

"What time is it?" Barbara asks.

"About three," Sadie says, distracted. She leans to look in the living room, to assure herself that Louisa's body is where her voice signaled. We should never be out of each other's sight, Sadie thinks. Something might happen.

"What?" Barbara asks. "Sadie, that's impossible."

"Yes?" Sadie says, but still looking at her other sister who slowly is approaching, and for a moment, one flash, a step, Sadie imagines Mother approaching to scold her for not winding the clock. *I didn't know, Mummy dear. You didn't tell me.* Louisa catches in midstep Sadie's expression, and stops, awkwardly, wondering what has happened to her youngest sister. Then, suddenly, the frightened child is replaced with a calm Motherly smile.

Now Louisa stops, arrested by Sadie's resemblance to Mother. The resemblance freezes into identification.

"Sadie, you look so much like Mother now it's—it's—" Louisa falters.

"I do?" Sadie smiles broadly; the resemblance disappears.

"You did a second ago."

"Oh," Barbara drawls out, "Sadie's always looked most like her."

"Yes, that's true," Louisa comments, now moving into the dining room.

"Really?"

"Of course," Barbara says. "You've always known that. It's been told to you since you were a little girl."

"No, no," Sadie says. "You are the one who looks like Mother."

"Me?" Barbara points at herself. "Don't be so stupid. I don't resemble her at all."

"Well," Louisa begins, with the distance at which her dissimilarity to Mother places her, "that's not completely true. You both resemble her, I think; but in different ways."

"Like?"

"Well, it's hard to explain. Barbara, I think it's your body—your almost slenderness—Mother was always trim, you know? And Sadie—"

"And I've grown so fat." Sadie giggles, patting her stomach.

"I wasn't going to say anything," Louisa teases. "But—"

"Oh, I know. It's getting out of hand, really. And it's all because of that delicious candy that Barbara sent us for Christmas!"

"Oh, so it's my fault that you've put on weight," Barbara says, laughing.

"Yes," Sadie says, in mock seriousness. "You know that I have no will power. And that candy is simply the most delicious thing I have ever eaten in my life."

"Louisa's the one who should have eaten the candy," Barbara says.

"Oh, no," Louisa says, "I have to watch my weight just like you do."

"That's not true, Looza, that's simply not true. Why, you've always been thin, and you've stayed thin."

"Well, it's because I've been careful."

"Oh, no," Barbara says. "I've seen you eat cheesecake."

Louisa smiles. "Cheesecake, yes. That is my weakness. And I have to agree with Sadie, that candy you sent is a close second."

"But you don't really have to worry," Sadie says. "Not like I have to worry but never really do worry enough."

"Sometimes, I wish I looked more like you," Louisa says. "It's not nice to be skinny. I can't really tell which I would rather be."

"What you really mean," Barbara says, "is that you wished you looked more like Mother."

"Barbara," Louisa says. "Please don't ever say that to me."

"I was just trying to be honest," Barbara says. "It's true, isn't it?"

"You have your wishes, I have mine," Louisa says, but the movement of fumbling for a cigarette causes her to stumble over the words, as she sticks the pack into her pocket, misses, stoops to pick it up, all in agitated silence.

"Looza—" Sadie breaks it.

"Don't call me that."

"But . . ." Sadie stands as if she is about to cry, but then, thinking better, modulates her voice. "There is nothing wrong with wanting to look like Mother, Looza, you shouldn't be ashamed of it. I think we all must want to look like Mother a little bit. Don't you think so? But really, we're just upset because we're so tired. I'm so tired I don't know what to do. I feel as though I could fall down on the floor and curl up and go to sleep right now for a very long time." Then, suddenly, Sadie tumbles to the floor in a fluff of lace and slip, a sleepy clown, bubbling with laughter. The sisters are grateful to her. But, separately, they wonder about resemblance.

Barbara: You come unexpectedly. I say things I don't mean. I am the eldest—Do I look like you? It doesn't matter. I have your name. I know my place is as the eldest with your name. But you come without warning me, and I don't know what I am saying.

Louisa: Where is the warm cache of secrets? It is cold, now? Where's the dream? Has it dried up? Up. I light a cigarette and think, I don't and I can't and I never will look like you at all. And I feel I am losing my powers to think differently.

Sadie: Dear God, give me a song to silence the fear in this

*lying asleep silly body. God be in my understanding like the
song and help me to understand what I don't. Oh, God, I am
afraid of myself, of little me made in the image of Mother.*

The words pass into bodies as resemblances, as family
traits, the mind of Mother trading places with the bodies
of the daughters. Perceived only as a whispering language,
she moves from the space outside into them. As one might
speak without hearing the words, these words rise up into
the daughters. And as the daughters themselves rise to continue to grab the silver and glassware in the dining room,
the snow, falling like seconds, stops, unnoticed.

SILVER

1 Asparagus Tong—*Sadie*
8 English Forks—Antique, South Carolina
   Buried in Convent Yard in Civil War—*Louisa*
4 Rattail Colonial Serving Spoons—*Barbara*

FIVE PAGES OF SILVER IN THE INVENTORIES' FIVE PAGES OF FORKS
and knives and spoons, jam spoons, sweetmeat dishes, serving
trays, flat silver and silver-plated ware, five pages from the
convent yard in the Civil War to the pantry at Buckingham
Palace. The daughters take the silver out of its boxes and
untie the stalks of knives and forks, laying them out on the
dining room table. All the silver is polished. It radiates under
the eyes of the chandelier.

Reed and Barton Tea Service—*Sadie*
12 Fruit Knives—Shell Design—*Louisa*
1 Pearl Handle Dinner Knife (English Rogers)—*Barbara*

The silver, more than the china, reflects the generations of the Luskins, the luncheon generation through to the cocktail party generation. The rows and rows of silver, however, gradually diminish in size.

Louisa, running her fingers over the engraved initials on the various pieces, initials that Sadie and Barbara are quick to match with names, never entertains. Barbara looks in disbelief at all of the silver, remembering the parties her mother held, luncheons and teas, but still she cannot imagine that Mother ever used all of it. No one entertains like that now. Barbara gives a dinner party only when her husband, a gourmet cook after his own fashion, feels like cooking—which is seldom and only for a few close friends. Sadie, however, enchanted by the Old Style, entertains frequently and on a large scale. She looks now at the silver, disappointed that she could not have used some of it for Maggie's engagement party (to which Maggie refused to come, though the adults, Sadie remembers, had a lovely time). At some point in the near future, Sadie will think of a reason to celebrate some event with Maryland crabmeat and champagne poured into the Luskin wine glasses with the family crest, which she, luckily, grabbed before Louisa had a chance.

1 Small Round Indian Tray—*Barbara*
1 Cake Dish with Handle—Antique—*Sadie*
1 Three-Part Pierced Edge Sandwich and Cake Dish—*Louisa*

During her mother's parties Louisa lay awake. Her bedroom was directly over the entrance in the old house, 1407. She remembers lying and listening: *The doors open, she hears hello . . . my goodness . . . sorry we're late, but . . . ; then the voices drift away to her left, into the dining room, where she can hear faintly the scrape and tap of eating, the pauses, the opening and closing of the pantry doors. She lies*

*there waiting for the day when she will be grown up, able to
talk and clink her glass; waiting to read what they had read,
the books which made the melodies of the conversations rise
and fall, stop and go, the books which made brandy in the
sitting room, the articles that made gossip in the living room.*

  2 Candle Snuffers—*Sadie*
  1 Tankard—Coin Top, Antique—Augsburg—*Louisa*
11 Dessert Spoons—"S.D.L."—*Barbara*

*It is late afternoon the day of Mother's party. Barbara has
been asked by Jewel to help polish the silver, now that Jewel
has conferred with Mother and been given the instructions
for the evening. Taking out the set Mother wishes to use,
Barbara begins methodically to polish the spoons, forks and
knives. Leaving the larger serving spoons (counted according to the number of dishes that will be served), and the
serving trays (according to the number of guests) for Jewel
to polish, Barbara puts her own polished pieces on the felt
over the dining room table, shaped into spoon fans, knife
tracks, and fork flowers. Mother rushes into the dining room,
a needle and thread and a blouse in her hand. —What are
you doing? —Helping Jewel. —And did Jewel instruct you to
make pictures with the silver? Is that your idea of helping
her? —No, Mother. —Well, I suggest you help her, then, and
not play. Dinner is in a few hours. Her hands wave through
the air to undo the magic of the silver laid out on the table.*

12 Oyster Forks—"L"—*Sadie*
  1 Child's Cup, Leaf Design—"Louisa Ann Luskin"—
    Louisa
  2 Large Serving Spoons—*Barbara*
  4 Small Salt Cellars, Repousse, Antique, with three
    spoons—*Sadie*

1 Sauce Bowl, Antique—"S.D.L."—1865—*Louisa*
1 Child's Cup—Chinese—*Barbara*
1 Small Hot Milk Pitcher (soldered)—*Sadie*

The cold surface of the silver is warmed by the lights of the chandelier to a golden tint; and warmed further by the three pairs of hands tracing the engravings of the initials, the lines of the Colonial Rattail spoons. They take their turns in a collective silence and continuous circular motion as the chandelier gently illuminates lips, cheeks, hair, suffusing the three women in a mixture of gold and silver light that softens the brittle tips of the Luskin wealth. The inexhaustible silver is repeatedly tagged with yellow, blue and red, red, blue and yellow, blue, yellow, red, as their hands fall onto the silver handles, selecting, their hands passing through the rainbowed air from one world to another. Their hands choose the silver as they imagine their mother chose, and her sisters-in-law chose and Grandmother Luskin chose to arrange future table settings at which children and their parents sat (and usually guests). The table settings, too, at which they were forbidden to sit as children.

The table is set. The guests have not yet arrived. It has been four hours they have been kept in their room, and Nurse has now unlocked the door, on schedule, to let them out to say good evening to Mother who sits in her room after a bath. Sadie sneaks out of the nurse's sight, down the stairs —quickly—into the dining room. Jewel sees her. She presses her fingers to her own lips and then to Sadie's. "Don't you say a word, now." Sadie follows Jewel into the kitchen. The food is just above her eyes. If she reaches up she can take it, but she will not know what she is taking. Jewel hands her a large cookie. "Now, run along before that Nurse finds you." Sadie

*bites into the cookie, wanders into the dining room: —rows
of silver just at the level of her eyes. The tips of the forks
line up into dots if she stands at exactly the end of the line.
She cannot see the blades of the knives, lying flat on the table-
cloth. The edges of the spoons dip into the air—Sarah Luskin,
what do you think you are doing in here?—I was just looking
to see what Mummy—Get upstairs immediately.—But I was
just*

*Nurse carries Sadie up the stairs screaming. It is another
four hours she will be locked inside the room and nothing
her Mother can do will change Nurse's mind.*

*As Sadie reaches the top of the stairs, she sees her mother's
arms reaching—an embrace?—No, the arms open and then
suddenly they are shut when the nurse tells the story over
Sadie's screams. No meals for two days, but she will sit at
all meals. Screaming, Sadie is carried into the room and
locked inside for four hours.*

    1 Grape Scissors—*Sadie*
    4 Tiffany Candlesticks—"B.K.L."—*Louisa*
    4 Gravy and Cream Ladles—*Barbara*

Their mother's arms opened when they learned to speak
like well-behaved little girls; then, they could be displayed
to the guests. They did not scream. They were no longer
locked in their room for four hours, according to the British
System. They had a new governess. They did not need to be
rescued. And over and over again they heard their mother say,
We do have our Code, you know.

Every Luskin woman is meant to live by the Code. It does
not apply to Luskin men; only to the women who bear the
name both before and after marriage. Though Da's sisters
took other names when they married, it was the Luskin Code

to which they adhered, and it was the Luskin Code that Mother took for her own, making herself more of a Luskin than the other women in her husband's family.

The Code expresses itself differently with each woman, though its demand is the same: Grandmother Luskin gave birth to nine children, whose ages spanned two generations. She made sure that her sons went to Yale and not to Harvard. She made sure that her daughters learned to play the piano in order to comfort their future husbands when they came home from a day at work. Grandmother Luskin sang "Beautiful Dreamer" on the Yale Green *after* attending church. And Grandmother Luskin watched an operation to remove a tumor from her stomach, demanding a mirror instead of anaesthesia. She was the first to keep records of her own life and to make them available in print to her family. She encouraged her daughters to do the same, so that there are now three generations of Luskin Records that have preserved the domestic ins and outs of the Luskin Family in female hands.

The records sort one generation from the next, explaining in minute details the cross-cousins, intermarriages, and the acceptances into Society, culminating in the New York Four Hundred list of worthies. But as these three women, the next generation, grab the silver, they feel unable to separate the children from the mothers, the sisters from the daughters, and the wives from the cousins, as the silver changes hands in circles.

> 1 Six-sided Tiffany Preserve Dish—*Louisa*
> 1 Small Indian Sugar Bowl—*Barbara*
> 1 Pair Early American Tongs—*Sadie*

These Luskin women—mothers, daughters, mothers- and daughters-in-law—started the Family News and bore children to continue the Family News. But they were not tender women. They managed husbands, children, and the complexities of family as a business. They were in control. The men they married were usually men not strong enough to dampen the female vigor. And the Luskin sons were themselves brought up by a mother who favored women over men. When they married, they felt that the name they gave their wives was the property of their mother as well as their father —but it was a mother who made the Luskin name important. As mothers, they hid whatever tenderness their sex prescribed; they were brutally honest and intelligently charitable.

They called on the Code as other women might call upon female intuition to guide them. The Code was a sanctuary for the uneasy hearts underneath their breasts. They were not masculine women; but they were set apart from other women because they ruled the house.

A Luskin mother never tells her daughter, "The Code means . . ." The daughter grows up, watching her mother over the years imitating the Luskin women who preceded her. She sees her mother beckoning the Code as she turns her head away. She overhears the Code on the other side of a door that will not open if the daughter cries. She catches a whisper at luncheon. She hears the Code passed down the laps with the hymnals at church. And in hospitals, dying, but refusing medicine, the daughter, by then herself a mother, watches the Code fighting the tumors that have also been passed down from one generation of women to the next.

All of Grandmother Luskin's daughters, except Sister Mathilda, died of cancer early. But the Code survived. For the women of the next generation rise to fit the Code to their world. As these three women grab at the silverware in the Luskin dining room, they grab at the generations of women preceding them, who entertained (before the cancer attacked) behind their husbands' backs, with their husbands' shoulders just in sight, framed in the doorway of the other room where the men debated the outcome of events beyond the home.

It was into the inner room their mother married. As her five sisters-in-law (all called "Sister") faded, four of them dying, it was Mother who took over. Perhaps it was discovering the tumor when she was in her mid-forties that made her fight to be more of a Luskin than the women who were born with the name. Perhaps it was the tumor itself that made her feel like a true Luskin woman. As her daughters lay their hands upon the stems of spoons they claim for themselves their mother's victory. She proved herself worthy of being a Luskin woman, attaining the Luskin silver, and with finality, the finality of a terminal disease, she disowned her origins utterly. When the doctors operated on her in her mid-forties, removing her uterus, the maiden Knowles died out.

Louisa, about to place her strip of red on a dish, notices a note, half hidden by the sweet plate with Medallion of Heads.

"What's this?"

"What's what?" Sadie moves closer to Louisa.

"This piece of paper," Louisa says, taking the note in her hands. The folds of the paper are broken, and the edges have yellowed. It is stiff Tiffany stationery on which all of Mother's personal correspondence was written. Louisa carefully unfolds it as Barbara moves to the other side of her. The sisters are in a line when their mother's handwriting, a black slant, appears.

When S.D.L., my mother-in-law, died, her collection of silver surpassed the expectations of her remaining chil-

dren. We gathered at the Virginia home for a reading of
the will. When the family lawyer read that the Luskin
silver had been bequeathed to me, Sister Mathilda fainted.
She was the only remaining daughter, and had expected
to receive the silver. But Sister Mathilda was barren.
When the will had been read through to the end, the
possessions remaining were left for The Family to grab.
After conferring with Da, we agreed that the bequest of
the silver and other assorted heirlooms was satisfactory.
We excused ourselves from the grab with the lawyer's con-
sent.
Sister Mathilda recovered suddenly from her fainting spell.

Signed, Barbara Luskin

The date of the note is missing.
"Well," Barbara says, "I guess that explains it."
"What?" Sadie says, still looking at the note.
"Why Mother has all of the silver. I've been wondering
how she could have gotten all of the Luskin collection."
"How strange," Sadie says.
"What?"
"That Grandmother gave it all to Mother."
"Oh, it's not strange," Barbara says, walking away. "It's
quite logical."
Louisa, placing the note down on the table between two
different sets of dinner forks, says, "I don't think it's logical
at all."
"Neither do I," Sadie says, flopping down on a chair. "It
doesn't make any sense. I mean, to me it doesn't make any
sense. I don't know why."
"You are both forgetting," Barbara says, her voice tired,
her body restless, "that Mother and Sister Mathilda were
the only remaining daughters. The note says that much."

"But how could that—"

"Sadie. Think."

"I am."

"Grandmother Luskin outlived her daughters."

"She would," Louisa says.

"Do you remember," Sadie says, "when we were little and we used to go and visit Grandmother in Virginia and how—"

"Sadie," Barbara says, walking around the room.

"But don't you remember how when we sat down—Oh, I remember it so well—because I couldn't eat, which isn't something that happens to me, I mean, I love eating, but— I remember how I just couldn't eat anything I was so nervous with a servant standing right behind me waiting to take my plate away. and I remember there was a servant standing behind everyone at the table and—"

"Do we have to go through another one of your fond recollections of childhood?" Barbara says.

"Not if you don't want to." Sadie pouts.

Louisa has not listened to their conversation. She now asks, "Barbara, why do you think Mother received the silver and not any of the others?"

"Well," Barbara says, "I don't think that she would have given it to any of her sons."

"But why?"

"I don't know why. What does it matter, anyway? Mother was given the silver. That's all that we need to know. We don't even need to know that. It's obvious."

"But she could have given it to Margaret or Sarah's children."

"But she didn't, did she?" Barbara looks over at her sister whose dark face remains puzzled. "What's bothering you?"

Louisa looks up. "Do you want to know?"

"I do," Sadie jumps in. She wants to know what is bothering herself, however, more than she wants to hear Louisa.

"What's bothering me," Louisa says, slowly, "is that Mother didn't participate in the grab."

"Yes, yes," Sadie lights up, "that's it! It's not that she was given the silver—that's kind of nice, really, when you think about it. As if Grandmother Luskin finally accepted Mother as part of The Family, you know, as a real Luskin and not just a married one, and I think it was awfully nice of her, really. Mother must have been so proud! Don't you think that Mother must have been terribly proud when she heard?"

"I don't know," Louisa says. "This note doesn't sound as if she liked it."

"But of course she liked it, Looza. Of course Mother liked it."

"But Mother was a Luskin before she married," Barbara says, irritated at her sisters who have not followed The Family tree as carefully as she has. She would not expect Louisa to keep track; but Sadie should have.

"I've never understood that," Louisa says. "I heard about it, but I never really understood it."

"It's quite simple. Mother and Da were third cousins."

"So that she was—" Louisa shakes her head. Her ancestry looks too complicated to understand as she stands among the surfeit of forks and knives and spoons. But what is puzzling her is that she had thought, until she read the note, that Mother must have acquired many of the objects in the house through the grab in Virginia. But the note says that she did not even stay for that grab. So that the objects now acquire mystery. Mother must have collected most of them herself. Louisa wonders why her grandmother chose to give the silver to her daughter-in-law. Not only her daughter-in-law, but the youngest, too, married to Da who was Grandmother Luskin's last son. But more, Louisa thinks about her mother's refusal to be in the grab. Her father's agreement also bewilders her.

"Why do you think Da didn't?" she says.

"Didn't what?"

"Didn't join in his mother's grab?"

"Because," Barbara says, now moving around the room, stretching, anxious to keep moving around the conversation, "he already had the silver, through Mother. And other things, apparently. He probably felt just as she did. That they had enough."

"I don't think that's it," Sadie says quietly from the chair. She has herself been wondering why Da didn't grab. She cannot imagine anyone refusing to be in a grab, especially what was probably the biggest grab of all.

"What do you think, Sadie?" Louisa says, feeling an uneasiness in her sister's words.

"I think—I think that men just don't care about grabs."

"Oh, Sadie," Barbara says from a corner of the dining room, "don't generalize." *Women are so goddamn materialistic and petty,* Barbara remembers. She does not remember Tom showing any interest in the grab. He removed himself into a corner and studied more diligently than usual the lectures he was to give the following semester. As if waiting for her to return, as if she had already left and he was preparing himself for the adjustment they would have to make. "You can't," Barbara repeats, "generalize like that. It doesn't say anything about anyone, really." *Do I know him? My husband? The man I made a "good pair" with, the tall blond man who trusted my judgment when we built the new house—for love? Was that the point?*

"I don't mean to generalize, Barb, it's just that it suddenly seemed to me that men just don't want to grab. I don't mean that they don't want to," Sadie pushes against the gold and silver lighting of her ancestry. "I mean, that they don't naturally want to. The grab is what women do. Luskin women, I mean, are supposed to grab, and maybe all women in some way. I really don't know why I am thinking this, it's just—it's just—I don't know what I'm saying. The Luskins are so complicated sometimes! So complicated and—and—"

"Certain Luskins are very complicated," Barbara says, her remark intended to stop Sadie's nonsensical (to her) rambling. "And," she continues, "manage to make simple things complicated."

"What are you getting at?" Louisa says, lighting up a cigarette. She is determined to keep the conversation going, especially after what Sadie has said.

"I am trying to get us to stop talking and start grabbing," Barbara says, reaching for her copy of the inventory to check to see if there is any more silver listed.

"Looza?" Sadie says. "What do you think?"

"Me?" Louisa now sits down in one of the chairs and picks up the note. Barbara remains standing, deliberately, shifting her weight from one foot to the other. "Well," Louisa begins, slowly, looking at the note. "I was just think-ink that it was odd that you would feel the way you do, Sadie. I mean," she tries, gently, "that of the three of us you would feel that the grab was—was female."

"Why?" Sadie says, then her hands go to her temples. "I don't know what I mean. It's not wrong, is it? It's not—"

"Of course not," Louisa says, avoiding Barbara's movements. She turns to look at Sadie. "But don't you have that list?"

"List?"

"The one that George made."

"Oh, that list. That?" Her hands fall. "I had to make him

sit down and write it out. He didn't want to at all. But I insisted that he do something! I was so upset, and, and, well —I thought that both of you wouldn't think it was a good idea, not really, to have any kind of grab before the grab. Oh, I know I wrote that letter. But that was before I persuaded George to write out his own list and—but he didn't care, you know? He didn't really care."

"I was wondering about that," Louisa says.

"Well, it doesn't really prove anything," Barbara says. In spite of herself, she is interested in the conversation and now begins to wonder why Tom trusted her judgment. He didn't really say anything to her. She knew he would want foreign things; or thought that he would.

"Well," Louisa says, half smiling where she sits between her two sisters. "We should at least all admit that whatever our husbands feel, we basically enjoy it."

"Oh, of course! Of course we enjoy it. And you know," Sadie says, "I think that Mother would have enjoyed it, too. Immensely."

"We certainly couldn't grab if we weren't her daughters," Louisa says.

"What?"

"I mean, if we weren't all a little grabby ourselves."

"Looza! Mother was the least grabby, the most unselfish woman I ever knew in my life. How can you—"

"You're contradicting yourself, Sadie," Barbara says.

"No, no, I'm not. I'm not contradicting myself. Just because I think Mother would have enjoyed it doesn't mean that I think she's selfish."

"I didn't say that Mother was selfish," Louisa says.

"Well, she wasn't," Sadie says.

"Mother never took anything that wasn't her right," Barbara says, "according to the Code."

"Oh, yes," Louisa says, putting out her cigarette, "according to the Code."

"And what's wrong with that?" From Barbara's point of view, Louisa not only shuns the Luskin Code, but has none of her own as a substitute.

"Nothing. Except," Louisa looks up, "sometimes I wish that Mother had done something—anything—that was not according to the Code."

"You do?"

"Yes, I do."

"But that was her great strength," Barbara says, "and was probably one of the reasons that Grandmother Luskin gave her the silver."

"Well," Louisa says, "I'm not sure."

"What have you been trying to get at?" Barbara says, finally giving in and sitting down. She stretches her legs out, straight.

"Here," Louisa holds up the note. "When we first read this it occurred to me that the one chance Mother had to be in a grab, she refused. Isn't that—odd?" Louisa looks from one sister to the other.

"But that's not true," Barbara says, wishing that she did not have to explain what she feels her sisters should know. Why is it that she is the only one of them, she thinks, who can keep The Family straight? "She was in Mathilda's grab. And so were we. That's where a lot of Grandmother's things ended up."

"Was she?" Louisa says. "I don't remember—"

"No, she wasn't," Sadie says. "I know she wasn't. Because I remember trying to persuade her to come and she said that she had plenty already and that she didn't want to."

"She didn't want to?" Barbara asks.

"Well, no, she didn't put it that way. She wouldn't. It was just after we were all married, and I remember how excited

I was. Weren't you? But Mother said that she thought that she had enough things already, and that she—I don't remember what she said, Barb. I just remember that she refused to go but I was so excited that I didn't think about it. I mean, not the way I think about it now."

Barbara remembers her own excitement, when she was younger. It had been simple, then, with so many distant relatives to round things out and no one, really, close to Sister Mathilda. It had been like a big party of cousins.

"So," Louisa says, "it seems that Mother managed to get herself out of it every time she had a chance."

"What do you think it means, Looza?"

"Simply that Mother never grabbed for anything," Barbara says, "that's all that it means. Although I'm sure that Louisa thinks Mother's refusals reveal something about her inner character."

"They might," Louisa says, though not wanting to get into an argument with Barbara. "Isn't it difficult," she says, louder, "to imagine Mother grabbing?"

"My guess is that she would have thoroughly enjoyed it," Barbara says, resisting Louisa's tendency to complicate Mother, "because she liked anything that was traditional."

"But not the grab," Louisa insists. "Apparently she did not like that Luskin tradition."

"I wonder why she made us go through it," Sadie says. "I mean, if she didn't, then why us?"

"Because the grab is a terribly efficient means of distributing property, and nothing more. Its economy would have appealed to her. Now," Barbara says, getting up, wanting to end the conversation before she finds herself doubting what she persists in thinking, "let's put an end to this pointless conversation."

"I can't imagine Mother grabbing," Louisa says, half to herself.

Grabbing at crying babes, frightened. But who was frightened?

Sadie gets up from her chair and walks over to the note. "What shall we do with it?" She picks it up. She is thinking, as she holds the stiff paper in her hand, of George, and how difficult it had been to persuade him.

"Leave it," Barbara says. "We've been through all of the silver, anyway." She turns the page of her inventory.

"But we can't leave anything, Barb. We can't leave anything."

"Then take it if you want."

"I do," Sadie says, putting it into one of the silver bowls she has already tagged blue.

The note lies there reminding them of Mother's marriage into a family she gradually claimed as her original. But she never grabbed.

As the three women leave the dining room, the grab changes course with their bodies. The trio, unpartnered by husbands, unsure of their mother's purpose, moves out into the back hall; and as they walk, they think of their own marriages in turn, of their husbands who seem to be standing in the wings.

IN
THE WINGS

MOVING INTO THE REAR WING OF THE HOUSE, THROUGH THE
back hall, they enter the sitting room that looks out over the
garden covered with snow, white-edged limbs of branches
glowing in the night under a cleared sky. It is cold where
they sit beneath their father's portrait; but, as they take turns,
the room gradually warms.

Sadie's turn: "Da when he was a little girl." A golden-
curled boy dressed in green velvet knickers tied with red
ribbons at the knees, his jacket buttoned with gold buttons
across his plump waist, tied with a long red sash, a little boy
out of another century, her father's portrait. He is the father
Sadie remembers, ostentatiously framed in golden wood-curls
and frills of flowers. He is the father Sadie loved, the daughter who giggles and wears lace, who goes to the country club
dinners, who smiles, who kisses her husband when he comes
home from work, who laughs at his bad jokes, bakes cakes
that he doesn't like to eat.

She married him when she was just twenty, looking thin and girlish in her bridal gown. Of the daughters, Sadie was the first to marry, but not to the man she first loved. She married the man who made her laugh the most, with his Southern accent, his slow way of drawing out a story, punctuated by Sadie's giggles. When they were married he was gentle with her; his face was soft at its corners, his lips full like his vowels; she trilled under his kisses, she sang.

Did she sing? Or did she panic before he came home from work, hearing the briefcase land on the hall chair? Did she rush up the back stairs to make sure the beds were made, fix his dinner, wait for him to finish reading the newspaper? Did she sing or did she vacuum the rug, buy the groceries, knit a sweater he wouldn't wear? Did she lose her first child, a boy, lose her second child, a miscarriage, and then give birth to a girl, singing? Did she sing as she gave birth to another girl? And another girl? Did she sing as she never gave him the son he wanted?

And then, with three girls dressed in the same sets of clothes, did she wait for him to finish reading the newspaper or interrupt him with stories of the little girls? And then, when they began to grow out of their clothes and were sent to school, did she get home in time to fix his dinner? Did she notice he was getting home later and later? Did she read the piece of paper he typed one Saturday morning he made her sign? Did she promise never to leave him? Did he sign it? Did he say he would never leave her?

And did she scream then? When her daughters were away at school did she scream? Or did she wait for him, wait for him to say Don't scream? Yes. She waited for him to say, "Now, dahling, none of that." Yes, she waited for what she knew he would always say to her, and she never screamed, she never screamed. She continued to sing in the kitchen, to sing at night to her frightened daughters, singing as they grew till she sang at Maggie's wedding, sang to the others who were left at home, sang when her husband left on business trips, and continued to sing when he said, Now, dahling, none of that, continued to sing—

I thought it was the spirit that moved you to song.

That song was crazy. You sang it just to spite me
I sang it to spite me
that song I sang and did not understand
avoid the dark
my marriage song that moves me to scream

December 12, 1943: Sadie stands beside her mother in front of the mirror adjusting her bridal veil. Outside there is no snow to match the falling lace and pearls. A heat wave has hit Washington and outside it is nearly seventy, warm but not too warm, a peaceful, pleasant warmth like the song in Sadie's heart. Mother, do I look beautiful?—A bride should look beautiful. Mother, should I marry?—A girl should marry. Mother, what is marriage?—Marriage? You will learn what marriage is sooner than you care to learn. Mother, I'm scared.—You cannot be afraid today. You must get ready to leave. You are getting married. Mother, I am the first daughter to get married. Are you happy for me, Mummy dear?—A mother is always happy when a daughter marries a good man. Is George a good man?—Apparently you think so. But Mummy, what do you think?—I think your bridal veil is askew. Mother adjusts the veil on Sadie's young head: above her blue eyes the rows of pearl stitched into the lace glimmering in the afternoon light.

Sadie stands, holding her breath. This is her moment.

And she is the first daughter. The others are older but they are not even engaged. They are only bridesmaids today. She is the only bride. Downstairs they wait for the bride. Upstairs the bride waits.

George, she thinks. George is the man I am going to marry. I'm going to spend the rest of my life with him. George. Not Harry because Harry made a fool of himself up at the lake. And anyway, what will become of such a man? But George, George from Georgia, he is the man who is going to take my hands and will stay joining hands joining lives forever, I do. I do and I will. She lets her breath out, takes one last look, and descends the stairs.

The family gathered oohs and aahs, just as Sadie imagined, and all so beautiful. This is the first wedding from the house, and she is filled with light, with happiness, reminding herself It is George I am going to marry, because he is a good man and will make something of himself and, besides, he comes from such a good family, and he makes me laugh, yes, there's the good family and they make me laugh. The other family, the Luskins, is a larger group, looking at her with approval, nodding their heads, her sisters nodding their heads with envy, her mother looking at her with concern—

Mother, I'm scared of marriage. —You cannot be afraid today. Today—I must sing.

And Sadie walks at the head of the procession on the arm of her father, across the street to the church and then into the church the procession following the beautiful bride into the beautiful church as the music begins to play and Sadie's body is filled with song, the song of her marriage, I do and I will

Do you take this man? I do.
Will you sing? I will.

Do you scream at night? I do.
Are you afraid of the dark? Yes.
Yes, yes, the music will silence the scream
Of the girl just twenty and not in love
Singing a love song I do

Yes, yes, the music will silence the scream
Of the woman just fifty and all alone
Singing a love song I will
Not scream.
It is the spirit that moves me.

Louisa's turn: "Da when he was a little girl." Louisa is relieved to see that Sadie has no apprehensions about taking the portrait. Louisa hates the portrait, a grotesque of her father. It is not a picture of the man Louisa likes to remember as her father. No; because in the freakish portrait he resembles Sadie when she was a little girl, and does not at all look like the man who was Louisa's father, who gave her eyes like his. Louisa is the only daughter who has her father's dark coloring, the large brown eyes and his sober silence. He was a quiet man who liked to listen more than to speak; who liked to know more than reveal what he knew. That man who was the editor of a now defunct newspaper was her father, not the little golden boy or the old bedridden invalid. She thought that he must know everything behind his thin, still lips. But she never talked to him. She never asked him questions.

No. She asked him one question. She asked, "Da? Do you like Patrick?" Her father nodded. "Why do you like Patrick?"

"He speaks well. He is further along in the newspaper world than I was at his age. He will go far." Her father paused, then smiled. "But I would give him the advice which was given to me when I was a young reporter."

"Yes?"

"Never lose your sense of superficiality if you want to get along in the newspaper world."

Louisa laughed. "Who told you that?"

"Believe it or not, it was Arthur Brisbane, at six A.M. in a train, as he was buttoning his pants."

Never lose your sense of superficiality. Wasn't that exactly what Patrick had lost? Or was superficiality what their marriage, condensed now in Louisa's mind, had lost, the gloss? Yes, the marriage had changed into a relationship, into something with words in it and knowledge and—

Betrayal: To speak words which lead to other words which lead to knowing. My place is to know. What do I know?

> I know my body is clothed in silence,
> and the silence is straight.
> I am different because I know and knowing
> know I betray. That I speak, and say
> I hate those women who are blond like my mother,
> whose hair curls.
> Please love them.

As Louisa remembers her marriage over the years she is struck by how much she does know about Patrick, as if all of the small things she knows about him add up to knowing him. He wakes up early, at quarter to seven every morning, and appears to be in the shower before he has left the bed. Before she gets down to breakfast she hears the car in the driveway. And she knows how proud he is that both his sons went to Yale; even prouder that their eldest is now at Yale medical school. Having a doctor in the family makes Patrick more determined to run on Saturday mornings. When their sons were small, they would go out with their father into the

backyard and toss the football. She would listen at the back
porch for her husband to say, "Oops. My fault," and move
closer so that the boys could reach him. He sails and argues
with his colleagues. When he comes into the house, he yells,
"I'm home." Her father was right. He did go far.

Louisa is secure now that her father approved of the man
she married. She is glad that he died before he could know
they were thinking of separating. But Mother—Mother never
got along with Patrick. Louisa remembers how they would
fight; Mother could not resist arguing with him. They
matched wits, yes, because both Mother and Patrick took
pride in a verbal dexterity.

But, Louisa thinks, Why did he stop? He did go far; but
he gave in.

"I want a divorce."

"Oh." He didn't argue. Why didn't he argue? Why didn't
he say, No? Why did he accept my betrayal? But then, after
the funeral, why did he say No then? When our marriage
was already missing, when it wasn't there?

June 9, 1945: The heat in Washington rises to a record 110
degrees. Everyone sweats. The bride sweats, the groom sweats,
hating the heat. The guests are dripping, the Luskins are all
wet under their dress coats. Louisa's satin is staining. Louisa
is late, late as rush hour. The procession has left, lagging in
the heat, trying to put on dry faces but thirsty, waiting for
the punch at the reception. Looking forward to the cool of
the church, the procession arrives ahead of the bride who
has forgotten her shoes.

Louisa runs back to the house across the street. No one
notices her missing for she left before anyone could notice.
She has gone rushing, hot, sweating back into the house,
now she is racing up the stairs tripping on her gown; the

servants exclaim, she yells, I forgot my shoes, the servants
laugh, Jewel laughs loudly and says, Oh, Looza, but you
always be forgetting something.

Louisa rushes into her room, grabs her ballet slippers and
without slipping them on she races back to the church now
almost dead with the heat, flat-footed, burning and dizzy as
it whirls up from the asphalt into her swishing gown, rushing
too fast Louisa does not feel the burning street, the door she
wants to get to the door.

The door is closed. She bangs on the door but the music
drowns her knocking. She bangs, she races to the side of the
church where the music is less noisy, she bangs and bangs.

Inside there is a murmur Where is the bride? The bride
is missing. Keep playing the music. Patrick sweats. Louisa
is missing, the bride is missing, keep playing the music—

Louisa banging frantic and nearly fainting at the back of
the church. At last it is opened. Her cousin, one of the ushers.
No. Not her cousin. "I'm the bride. It's my wedding in there
and I'm not there. Look, I'm in my wedding dress, and I'm
not there. He'll think I've stood him up, Patrick will think
I've stood him up but I haven't, see, I'm here, and he's there,
and we're both supposed to be there, and I love him, please
I—"

"It's all right, miss."

She rushes in past the janitor, forgetting to put on her
shoes, through the back of the church. At last she reaches the
side of her sweating husband-to-be. Her shoes are in her hand.
Quickly she tucks them in between their arms. He smiles.

Patrick, I'm here, I'm here but

Oh my god, I'm getting married barefoot.

Louisa got married at the wedding when the bride was
missing.

Do you take this woman who is missing? He did.

He did take me, though I wasn't there. I was someplace else, although I didn't know where I was I was someplace else looking for something which I found but then forgot. If I ever find it at all, I'll find it in this house.

Barbara's turn: "Da when he was a little girl." Barbara cannot imagine her father looking like the little girl in the portrait. Not that Sadie had to take it so calmly, but, nevertheless, she is glad to know that she is not burdened with the painting. She could have taken it, as the eldest; but she could never have found a place for the old and decorative painting. So let Sadie have it, Barbara thinks. She probably likes it. And not that Barbara dislikes it; she simply has no place for a painting of her father in her house.

She wonders how Sadie could stand to look at that image of her father, distorted, not at all the way he really was. He was a kind man who told Barbara stories when they sat together by the lake. Sitting there, they would talk to real frogs, Barbara practicing the sound her father made. And there they would make up stories about the Frog Band. Well, Barbara laughs at herself. The Frog Band is certainly as silly as the portrait.

But no; because the stories about the Frog Band, a little orchestra of china frogs who look civilized compared to the frogs in the lake, were what the father and his daughter shared. Their friendship was rare when she was growing up, but something which was still approved of. Even Mother seemed to take pleasure in the tenderness between her daughter and her husband; or so now Barbara remembers, with a memory salve. She likes to think that she is remembering her father as he really was, as she guessed her mother must know him. Barbara never thought that there could be any antagonism between her mother and father, only comradeship, only sharing. She never looked below the surface, where she might have found tension between the man who was bedridden for twenty years and the woman who edited his dictations for the newspaper. She does not remember the bedroom; she remembers the boats and trains of her parents' trips off to India and Paris, promising to bring gifts back for each of them.

It will be my gift, I will be bringing back to my house . . .

Barbara suddenly doubts herself. Maybe she is telling herself something not quite to the point. *The romance of such a marriage.* Which marriage? Hers wasn't romantic. What was romantic was what she left when she married. Wearing her mother's wedding gown was romantic; and every corner of the old house, 1407, seemed to expand at the hour of her wedding, smelling of flowers from the florist's. It was the marriage of the Luskins' eldest daughter, and therefore a marriage to be talked about, to be praised in the upper social circles, to be written up in the newspaper. It was a Luskin fault to sentimentalize, and Barbara hates the sentiment that swathes her memory. *For love? But that's not the point, now.*

The point now is that she has been happily married to a wonderful man for almost thirty years. That is the point. And what was the point, then, when the corners of the house did not intersect, when both Sadie and Louisa were married? She was left, the eldest who should have been married first but married last and then suddenly, on impulse?

It is the only impulsive thing I've ever done in my life. Immediately after, everything was set, the corners were angled. Her marriage settled into the comfortable routine one would expect of two sensible people who both wanted the same things, who never argued, who trusted each other and maintained their mutual respect, two sensible people who married on impulse. They devoted themselves to making their marriage the ideal team, after suddenly making the goal.

Barbara was going to marry another man. She was engaged when she met Tom. For a moment Barbara forgets to remember the other man's name—she never thinks of him—but then she gives in and remembers his name was Joseph. Yes, Joseph Scott. With auburn hair and green eyes he flashed into her life; within a year he had won her, though at first she resisted. Always off on mad excursions, canoeing in unknown rivers, rowing at the head of the Charles, rock climbing, she was drawn to him, anxious for those thrills her upbringing strictly forbade her. Her upper-class upbringing, and her sex. So, one day, she agreed, excited, to marry him. He kissed her hard on the lips. Barbara rushed home to tell her mother, and her mother, contrary to what Barbara expected, approved. Although, Mother said, he is not as responsible a young man as one would wish for a husband.

Barbara postponed the wedding indefinitely. Joseph, frustrated, was willing to wait; he simply took more trips. While he was away, writing her letters describing the scenery, she began to think about why he loved her. From his point of view, she was quite a catch, as they said then, for he was not of her class. To marry her would mean a climb in the social circles. A step forward into the right society. They spoke that way then. Right society, good matches. But the phrases merely passed her by. She waited for him to return.

Before he returned, she met Tom, quite by accident. He was the quiet friend of her roommate's boyfriend, visiting for a weekend. He was not driven like Joseph; he was quietly determined. Determined enough to arrive on the doorstep of the house in Washington the same weekend that Joseph was to return. Mother answered the door, lifted her eyebrows and pursed her lips. Well, she exclaimed when Barbara came downstairs. There's a man who knows how to get what he wants.

Later she confided to Barbara, His eyes are too close together. But he is quite a pleasant young man.

Of course, Barbara's mind was settled. She broke off her engagement with Joseph that same weekend, and three weeks later she married Tom.

July 23, 1947: Everyone who was anyone came to the wedding of Barbara Mary Luskin to Thomas Alcott Fine. The best of Washington society gathered together on a humid day in the middle of July; The Family stuck in the muggy air. Barbara's wedding gown, adjusted to fit her solid, athletic body, glows around her. She is nervous; she sits down on the chair in her room, then gets up, then sits. Then she gets up, afraid she is wrinkling the dress. The dress is beautiful, but she wants to get out of it as soon as she can. The heat clings to her face like the silk tight down her restless arms.

Tom rushes into the bedroom, standing tall and handsome in his morning suit. Suddenly, as if for the first time, Barbara sees that her husband is handsome, blond, healthy, strong. She feels, as he kisses her once, without any shyness, that at this moment, before they have taken their vows, she loves him. Are you sure? Yes.

And as she walks down the stairs, holding onto the banister for support, the last Luskin daughter to be married, taking her father's arm and warmly squeezing it, as they walk side by side out the front door of 1407, winding down the spiral staircase out onto the street, pausing for a photograph, she thinks of her mother and her sisters, with their husbands following her. I'm the bride. They are wives. The procession walks in a slow and stately line to the church, and Barbara feels that she is leading the entire Family to her wedding, she is leading the generations of Luskins in a line. As she enters up the steps to the church she knows that this marriage is the right one, that they do make a good couple, are well-matched.

But her dress sticks, the slip underneath sticks to her stockings and she cannot breathe, the air is oppressive, there is no light in the solemnity, the humidity, she is the last daughter, this is the last wedding of her generation, and she feels on her head covered with itchy lace the burden of being the last one to marry, walking ahead of her sisterwives. She glances at Tom as she stands at the end of the aisle, trying to focus his features more distinctly. She wants certainty: the certainty of his profile, the aquiline nose, and his square chin placed on a long neck which, at this moment, seems to be stretching up, as if to reach an upper level of cool air. As she walks up the aisle, toward his profile as it changes into his face, she looks for the blue eyes which slope at their tips quietly, and she cannot hear the bridal march, she thinks only of his eyes and the line, the line of Luskins which she is about to carry on. She makes certain that every gesture will not reveal her fear as she meets Tom's eyes; every gesture must be certain, must be perfectly bridal, must be Barbara Mary Luskin and not yet, not yet Mrs. Thomas Fine.

She reaches the altar without stumbling, Tom's profile now close beside her, closer now than she thinks it will ever be. She remembers that brides can be a little nervous; so she tightens her hold on Tom's arm just a fraction of an inch, just as much as her wedding gown had to be adjusted.

I love him; and this whole performance is the performance of our faith in love——no, not our faith, but our love which promises, because it is ours, that the Luskin line will continue into the next generation, the promise to honor and obey, to love and to cherish, to honor and obey—

> to obey the line from which I come,
> and honoring the name of Luskin
> I honor your name,
> and obeying my past
> I will obey my future

But let's hurry, let's get to the part where we say I do and we kiss and you and I walk back down the aisle and out onto the street and quickly back to the house where we stand in the reception line and then when it's all over we can change our clothes and breathe again, I want to breathe again, breathe the air of Mrs. Tom Fine, quick, quick, let's get to that part, the part where we kiss and I'm Mrs. Tom Fine and you are Mr. Tom Fine and we're married till death do us part, Oh, why is it taking so long? When do I say it, when are we married, when does the ring slip on my finger, my grandmother's ring saved for me?

Till death do you part? I do.

I do, till death and only death part us, Mr. and Mrs. Tom Fine walking down the aisle past the crowds of family, past the already married sisters, past my father, past Mother, and out, quickly, out into the street and back home for something cool, cool for Mrs. Tom Fine's throat, quick, let's get out of these clothes and into our own, I am so hot, thirsty. I am married.

But it wasn't my death or his death, no, it was her death, which split into our space, intruded into our house. It was her death which is now making me remember the name of Joseph Scott who's probably dead in some goddamned avalanche.

And so what if my marriage was the only impulsive thing

I've done in my life? So what if I wasn't sure what his face looked like? We're best friends, and we've been happily married for almost thirty years. We still make a perfect couple. We are still sure of the certainty of our gestures. We've got our corners. We've made a good team.

So why am I disappointed? Afraid?

The impulse proved to be the right one. We're settled. But then she died and everything began to change
for better or worse
everything is about to change.

Her daughters stand up and leave the room.

IN
THE KITCHEN

SADIE SIGHS. HALFHEARTEDLY SHE TURNS THE PAGES OF THE inventory to the heading KITCHEN AND PANTRY. Suddenly, she realizes that they haven't had any dinner. "Oh, I'm famished," she says.

"So am I," Barbara says. "And thirsty. Let's go into the kitchen and eat something. Maybe we could divide up the kitchen while we're eating—there isn't that much to worry about in there."

"Isn't there?" Sadie asks.

"Well," Barbara says, entering the kitchen, "Mother didn't eat much when she was alone."

"That's true," Sadie says, following her. "She ate like a bird."

Louisa walks into the pantry, anxious for a drink. As she pours some Scotch from a decanter into a glass, she hears Sadie exclaim from the kitchen that it is already past midnight.

"What difference does it make what the time is?" Louisa says.

"Oh, I don't know," Sadie says, "It's just that it's so late and I didn't realize it, that's all."

"Well," Louisa carries the Scotch into the kitchen, "it doesn't mean anything—I'd just as easily believe that it is four in the afternoon."

Louisa and Barbara sit at the small kitchen table while Sadie fixes a dinner of sandwiches and fruit. They eat without talking, concentrating on the food which, put before them, increases their appetites. Louisa, however, begins to lose her appetite as Sadie finishes off her second sandwich; and then, when Sadie gets up, offering everyone ice cream, Louisa reminds Sadie about their conversation about weight.

"Oh, but I can't possibly resist ice cream! It's my favorite thing in the world! Won't you both have some?"

"I don't know about Barbara, but I'll just have a cigarette."

"None for me, thanks," Barbara says. "Just some coffee." She opens her inventory. "Now, let's see—why don't we just get these rooms done quickly and then go to sleep so that we'll all be ready for tomorrow?"

"Good idea," Louisa says, opening her copy of the inventory.

The grab in the kitchen, over coffee, runs smoothly, augmented by the late hour and the lack of interest in kitchen things. They are not valuable, only superfluous. They have no connection with the Luskin past, but only connect with the immediate past of Mother and the meals she didn't take. All three of the daughters want to finish quickly, averse to the memories of Mother's emaciated body. But then, Sadie, about to take her turn, runs out of tape.

"There's some more on the mantel in the living room," Barbara says. "I'll go—"

"No, no. I'll get it."

Barbara nods. As Sadie walks through the hall she hears the plates in the sink and the sound of running water over loose silverware. She stops, suddenly, in front of the portrait. The hallway is only lit by the small table lamp below the portrait, spreading out in a triangle over the canvas. But Mother's eyes are lit by the blue in her youngest daughter's look, unable to move, Sadie staring into the eyes, wondering what to say.

Mummy? Weren't you hungry? Didn't you eat anything, empty bird? Mummy, you did say it was all right, didn't you? To take? I know, I know; you must be happy that we're all home again. It must be nice to see us here together, all three of us. And to know that everything is staying in the family.

She does not hear the footsteps in the hall, approaching. She is absorbed in her murmuring.

But I have to apologize for the others. They don't know how we're not supposed to be fighting. You see, they don't understand yet. They keep on acting as if you weren't here. They keep on saying things that I know you don't think they should say. They forget. And—and, Mummy? I'm afraid of them.

Now Sadie hears a voice, lifting into a question, but it sounds distant, and echoes the way voices echo in church. Inside she continues her prayer to Mother which now begins to crescendo up and out of her.

They are taking everything from you because they don't understand that you're just giving us all these things because you love us so much. Mummy, I feel like singing but, Mummy, you won't leave your little Sadie behind, will you? Mummy, you did sing, once, didn't you?

Sadie's arms now move up to her throat.

Mummy, I'm full. I don't want any more.

They reach her throat and grip to stifle the scream that suddenly wells up out of her.

Don't let the dark eat me up

"Louisa! Louisa, what are you doing! Get your hands off of Sadie." Barbara rushes down the hall, then throws her arms around Sadie, who stands dazed beside a silent Louisa. Sadie is smiling at them both but without seeing them. Barbara then, without a word to Louisa, leads Sadie back into the kitchen. Louisa watches the two figures pass through the hall into the dark, then sees them outlined in the light of the kitchen door.

She turns. She faces the portrait. The portrait, unchanged, still hovers in the light, Mother's command fixed in her eyes. Louisa says nothing to her. It is Louisa's one moment of prayer. She turns from the portrait, numb.

In the dark hall, heading toward the voices in the kitchen, she pauses, putting her hands to her breasts. Each hand covers each breast, and rests, for a moment, covering them. Then, she removes one hand; then, the other falls off.

As Louisa enters the lighted kitchen, Barbara says, "Sit down. You look terrible." Barbara, determined to reconcile Sadie with Louisa after what just happened, demands

Louisa tell her "exactly what happened, from your point of view. Then Sadie will tell me hers."

"No, no," Sadie says, "I want to go first." Barbara touches Sadie on the shoulder.

"Okay. But don't exaggerate. It is a Luskin fault to exaggerate and I don't want to hear anything but what really happened."

Louisa gets another Scotch in the pantry; Sadie waits for her to return and sit down. Remaining silent, Louisa gulps down the Scotch and places the glass on the table. The liquor stings; pain revives her.

Sadie looks from one sister to the other, not knowing where to begin or what to say. "Well," she pulls at the lace of her frills, "I—but Barbara, I don't know what happened. Nothing happened. Oh, Looza, why did you do that?" She reaches out to touch her.

Louisa retracts her shoulder. "I didn't do anything," she says. "You must have imagined the whole thing."

"No, I didn't, I'm sure that I didn't imagine anything. It was clear. It was all clear for the first time in my life, it was all clear. I saw everything so clearly—oh, but how can I tell you? You must understand it because you saw it, Looza, you were there."

*Louisa: She is mad. My little sister staring at me is mad. Her hysteria's erupted, she's—*Louisa notices that Sadie's face does not glow; her eyes are less luminous. They do not reflect, but emanate a new shade of blue, a shade that looks, to Louisa, not like madness, but its opposite.

"Sadie," Barbara says. "Tell me what happened." Barbara looks over at Louisa, and with a blink Louisa realizes that Barbara thinks she attacked Sadie.

"Barbara," Louisa says, coughing. She clears her throat.

"Barbara, I didn't do anything. I don't know what Sadie is talking about."

"That's a lie!" Sadie screams. "That's a lie! You know perfectly well what I am talking about. It was all clear, I keep telling you, it was all clear, it was absolutely clear. Why do you deny it? Why don't you tell her?" Sadie screams. "Tell her yourself what it was."

Barbara's deep voice overcomes Sadie's shrill, "Stop it! Hold on to yourself, Sadie."

"Okay, okay," she says, "I can control myself now." Sadie looks into Louisa's eyes. Louisa understands nothing. The air is locked. "Look," Sadie says, quietly, trying to steady herself. "I'm all right. That's what I'm trying to tell you. I'm all right."

"But you . . ." Louisa begins. Then it occurs to her, as the air gradually loosens itself between them, that she, not Sadie, might have imagined it. *But no; that's impossible. Barbara says something. She sits there accusing me.* "What did I . . ."

"That's just what I am trying to get out of you two," Barbara says. "If it was so clear, one of you must be able to tell me."

"What did she do?" Sadie says. Then, looking over at Louisa, Sadie remembers what Louisa did after Mother's funeral. She reaches out across the table and offers her hand to Louisa. Louisa grabs it. They breathe, holding each other's hands, unable to speak.

"What?" Barbara says. "Look," she touches their hands in an effort to undo them. "Please tell me what happened. Is it so difficult?"

"Yes," Louisa says to Barbara, but looking at Sadie.

"Yes," Sadie echoes, "it is difficult to tell you." Sadie stresses the last word. Barbara's arms find themselves pressing against the edge of the table.

"When I came into the hall I saw something terrible. And now you two are sitting here all lovey-dovey. It doesn't make any sense."

"But it does," Sadie says. "It makes perfect sense. That's what I've been trying to tell you. You see, Louisa and I understand perfectly, don't we?" Sadie smiles.

Louisa removes her hand. "Sadie," she says, cautiously, "I know it will be difficult, but can't you tell me what is so clear? I'm afraid I think I understand it one minute and then I don't the next. Couldn't you just put it into words for me?"

Barbara's arms relax. Sadie, disturbed that, after all, she will have to explain, rubs her eyes. "Oh, I'm so tired. Can't we—?" But the closeness of the air between the three of them will not permit her to delay the explanation. "Okay," she says, sighing. "Okay, I'll try.

"I was standing there—that is, in front of the portrait, praying." Barbara scowls, then replaces a concerned mask. Louisa sits immobile, anxious to understand the words Sadie is speaking. Sadie continues, unabashedly frank, and, while her confession presses upon her to be adult and serious, she continues in her open childlike way to describe without considering the consequences. Her feeling of absolute clarity sustains her: she did understand and still does understand what at that moment she felt intensely and absolutely. "I was in front of the portrait, praying," she repeats. "I mean, it just came over me and I found that I was praying. I couldn't seem to help it. It just came over me that I wanted to say something to her and so I was there, praying. I mean, I guess that's what you would call it. I can't really think of another name for it."

Sadie, what are you doing?
I'm praying.
You're what?
I'm praying to Mother.
Sadie, are you all right?
Yes. I'm fine. I'm just praying to Mother. It feels good to
talk to her.
Are you

"Anyway, there I was when Louisa asked me what I was doing. At least, I don't remember it exactly, I mean, I wasn't hearing her then, but now I remember she said something to me. She said—" *crazy?* Sadie falters. She looks at Louisa, but Louisa stares at the empty glass in front of her trying to remember, concentrating. "She asked me if I was crazy. Mad. So I told her I wasn't because I wasn't crazy at all. I was just praying. I was just sort of full of things I wanted to say to Mother, full to bursting. And it was so clear to me that I wasn't crazy, I was just full, it was so clear, except that maybe we are all crazy, that occurred to me, too, maybe we're all kind of mad and crazy because of being here and forgetting, and forgetting—oh, it's so sad sometimes and it's all so difficult. It is difficult. I mean, I start to feel like we're all doing something wrong. I feel like a cannibal. It's terrible. But we're all cannibals if I am because we're all doing the same things and even I forget sometimes, yes, sometimes I do forget and I feel like a cannibal until I remember. But I didn't say any of that. That was just what I was thinking, sort of. I mean, it was sort of thinking."

The only prayer is the prayer that does not ask.

"I was just so full and suddenly I didn't want to be so full.

I guess, now, that I feel that way because it's such a relief not to want anything. It feels so sane to want nothing. So when I pray I want nothing and that's what it was to be praying then, that's what it is to pray right now in this house." Sadie looks up. The wish to tell all, to confess her entire heart to her two sisters sitting listening, begins to take hold of her, pushing the words out of her lips.

"Oh," Sadie sighs, "it feels so good to talk. I was afraid to talk before but the more you talk the easier and nicer it is. I never knew how good it could feel just to say things this way, real things, things from inside. That's part of what I understood. I mean, Louisa says things because she understands herself and says things from the inside. She's always thinking, you know? Always thinking. I used to be so frightened by her thinking. I thought she could see everything, I thought she was always looking into my mind and it frightened me because—because I don't like looking into my own mind. I hate psychologizing and all that. But this is different, now. I mean, you can look into your own mind and find something that you feel from the inside. I'm not thinking now. That's what's so nice about speaking. I'm not thinking at all; I'm just saying what I feel and you know, Looza? Barbara? It's such a relief to speak. All these words, I can't seem to stop them. I can't possibly tell you all the words that are floating around in my head that want to get out. So many words! You see, Looza, I do understand. That's what I'm driving at in this silly way.

"Oh, I know I'm silly. It's nice to be silly sometimes. Even all the time. That's what I was trying to tell you when I said that I wasn't any crazier than the two of you. I was trying to tell you that I really do know how silly I can be. You think I'm a baby. Well, you're right. I am a baby. I was acting like a baby in front of the portrait. I am a baby,

I know. But I—I like it. It's the way I've always been. I'm the baby in the family. You know, you both underestimate me."

"I guess we certainly have," Barbara sighs, sitting back in her chair. Sadie smiles broadly, her eyes glittering a deep and wonderful blue. This is Sadie's moment of victory. Louisa and Barbara listen, ashamed, baffled. Barbara understands only part of what Sadie is saying. Somewhere in the mess of words flying out of Sadie's mouth her little sister is growing up. But she never thought that Sadie was a child. She just treated her like one, natural as the eldest to the youngest daughter; because Barbara was the eldest sister, her other sisters needed to be looked after. She never put any conscious thought into it. Sadie just saying that she liked being the baby—that makes sense to Barbara. Because she . . . but Barbara's train of thought is interrupted. About to think, Because I like being the oldest, suddenly inside she knows *I hate being the oldest. I give up.* Barbara looks around the kitchen. In a moment she will cry. She must do something. She gets up and, going over to the sink with the half-done dishes, she runs the water in the tap. Then she stops. She doesn't want a glass of water. She wants some milk. Going over to the icebox, she takes it out and pours herself a glass.

"Me too, Barbara, me too," Sadie says.

"Louisa? Would you like a glass of milk?" Louisa murmurs No, thank you. She wants a cigarette, but she's smoked through her second pack of the day. She doesn't have the strength to go upstairs to get another pack out of the carton. She is thinking, or trying to think, of what Sadie has just said, wondering what, if anything, will follow. But she is stuck on Sadie's last sentence, wondering if there's any truth in it. Did she underestimate her little sister? And if so, why?

Out of a wish to be like her, a repressed wish—No. She never wanted to be either of them. Her whole life has been built up around her marked difference, physically and intellectually, from her two sisters. She has made her strangeness her strength. No, she underestimates Sadie just as she underestimates Barbara, and for the same reason. To magnify her difference.

"Where was I?" Sadie asks, and waits.

"You were talking about how we underestimated you," Louisa says.

"Yes," Barbara says, "about how you liked being a baby."

"Oh," Sadie says, smiling. "That's right. I do. I really do. I think, now, that it's always bothered you both in different ways. It does, doesn't it? Oh, it won't hurt me if you admit it, really. Yes, well, that's what I was beginning to realize when I was praying and talking to Mother. And to Louisa. She looked so—I don't know how to describe it. It was like she was there and wasn't there. And then she was so much there, so much that I—I . . . What did I do?" Sadie looks at her sisters, confused, and remembers, suddenly, that she was supposed to tell them something that she's forgotten. "Looza!" Sadie begs. "Looza, what did I do? I did something, didn't I?"

Louisa cannot tolerate it. Why must Sadie always disappoint her, just when she is tricked into expecting something from her? "Ask Barbara what you did," Louisa says, as she turns her empty glass in her hands. "Ask Barbara. She knows."

She rises, her glass of milk empty, dulled glass, coated with milk streams. Barbara stares at the glass and Louisa, at Louisa's glass.

"The glasses," Barbara says, mesmerized by the milky cylinder.

Louisa looks up at Barbara, thinking: Oh my God, now she's gone. Sadie stares at Barbara, frightened as she realizes that Barbara has lost control and she has lost control and Louisa's angry and everything is about to burst on everyone. She had looked up to Barbara for an answer, the accusation and bitterness of Louisa's statement passing Sadie by. Sadie thinks, No, no, Barbara will not lose control. Barbara always knows what's best. She's always right.

"What did you say?" Louisa says to Barbara, knowing that she is forcing Barbara to submit, now, to her will, she is gaining control over Barbara by demanding that Barbara, the honest one, be straight.

Barbara's eyes are glazed. Her body tense, ready to fly out at Louisa, to smash her sister's dark strange face. Barbara picks up the glass and, her hands shaking, she aims. Louisa ducks. But Barbara does not throw the glass; she smiles at her sister. Sadie is about to yell.

"I'm not going to throw this glass at you, Louisa," Barbara says. "And Sadie, wipe that expression off your face. It doesn't suit you." Sadie opens her mouth then shuts it automatically. "No," Barbara continues, "I just want to show you this glass. You see how it is covered with milk, and it is white and looks sort of like ice cream? You see that?" Barbara holds up the glass.

"Well, that is what happened. That is what is happening to us. That empty glass in front of you, Louisa, is who you are. And Sadie and I, our glasses are who we are." Sadie looks at her glass, then up at Barbara's, naively relieved that they look exactly the same. She doesn't understand what Barbara is saying, she only knows that her glass is like Barbara's glass so that means that they are on the same side. *But a moment ago it wasn't that way. It was . . . I was holding Louisa's hand and then I started talking about be-*

ing a baby and it all made sense. It did, it did. And now everything's lost. What has happened? What is happening to Barbara?

Barbara continues, levelly. "The glasses that have milk in them—they don't look empty. They look like there's still milk in them. But yours is completely empty. It has nothing. It is drained clean." Louisa looks at her glass. It is true; there isn't a drop of liquid in it. But . . . *How does Barbara know? She wasn't there. She's too stupid.*

"I'm not stupid," Barbara says, gaining mastery over Louisa slowly. "I know what you're thinking. You're thinking, How can my dumb older sister talk so symbolically? Well, it seems that everyone's been underestimating everyone else. You've always thought that I had no imagination. Well, maybe up till now I didn't. I didn't have to use it. But this changes everything. These glasses change everything. What's happened changed everything."

"Yes, it has," Sadie blurts out. "That's what happened: Everything changed all of a sudden. So I—Oh my Lord!" Her sisters are staring at each other. It's happened again, Sadie thinks. "Help, stop it! Stop it!" Sadie screams. "Stop hating each other! You can't. You can't, not now, not here. She won't allow it, she won't!" Sadie, after all, does understand. She understands what none of them have admitted: They hate each other.

"Who won't let me?" Louisa snaps at Sadie, her arms straight and stiff at her sides. "Who won't let me? Don't give me any of that. Both of you have been waiting for me to say it, isn't that so? You've been waiting for me to come out with it all day, even before it happened. You've been just begging me to say it. Because you know, now. You wanted to see if I knew. Well, I hope you're satisfied. I do hate." She glares at the two of them.

"No, no, you've got it all wrong. That's just what we didn't want you to do. That's—why, that's the reason we held hands. Don't you remember? We held hands because we were not going to say it. We understood each other. We held hands because we weren't going to let it happen again and we were sorry that it had happened at all."

"So that's what happened," Barbara finally speaks. "Louisa did attack you. I thought so." Louisa puts her face inside her hands.

"Barbara, how could you?" Sadie says, horrified. "How could you accuse Louisa of such a horrible thing?"

"But Sadie," Barbara says, "you just said it yourself." Sadie blinks; shakes her whole body. She looks as if she is about to get sick.

"Did I say that?"

"No," Louisa raises her face. Tears run down her cheeks, silently. "No, Sadie, you would never say a thing like that. You couldn't. You trust us, don't you?"

Sadie nods, ready to cry at the sight of Louisa's tears.

Barbara addresses Louisa stiffly. "She shouldn't trust you. Not after what you did to her."

"Barbara," Louisa says. "Barbara, did Sadie really say that I attacked her? Is that what you heard her say?"

Barbara cannot say yes, now, because she never actually heard such a thing. "She may not have said it outright, Louisa, because she can't bring herself to. But she would say it if she weren't being so considerate of you." Louisa, utterly broken, past caring for herself or what happens, past caring for consequences or outcomes, past even caring whether she says something or not, past all feeling but the dark wet feeling of tears and exhaustion, looks into Sadie's face. Sadie is now the judge.

Sadie looks at Louisa, then to Barbara, and bursts, expectedly, into tears.

"Oh, God," Barbara says. "Why do women always cry?"

Sadie is murmuring and her murmuring is getting louder till finally over her tears can be heard, "Why do you do this to us? Please, please don't do this to us. We can't stand it anymore."

Barbara asserts herself. "Someone should apologize."

"You," Louisa says, quickly, catching her breath. "You are the worst of all. You stand there, lording it over the two of us with your goddamned oldest-sister authority as if we were both children, both of us. If anyone should apologize, it's you, it's you for bringing us all to this extreme. You realize that, don't you? With your imagination? You can see, can't you, that this is all your fault? Completely your fault?"

"I didn't do anything," Barbara says, as yet unruffled. "I just asked you both what had happened, as any sane person would have. You are the one who's brought yourself to this."

"Oh, no I haven't," Louisa says, flashing. Her tears now stick dry to her cheeks. "You're wrong. You are completely and absolutely wrong. We didn't do a goddamned thing. You got that straight? Nothing happened. You were the one who wanted to have it all out in the open. You and your goddamned honesty. You always want everything out in the open, as if that's going to clear the air or dispel any bad feelings. That's how you approach everything. Well it's a bunch of crap. Lay your cards on the table; get it out of your system; be straight—that's all you ever say. Well it's bullshit, I tell you, bullshit. You hate secrecy, don't you? You're afraid of it, aren't you? That's why you have to pretend that everything's always out in the open. Well, who was the person who didn't mention it when something she loved was taken from her? Who was the person who didn't want to discuss it? You. You were the one who kept it bottled up. And look at you now. You're terrified of me. You're terrified because I'm being straight for one minute, just one lousy time I'm being straight and you're so goddamned scared that I'm not being secretive and mysterious, you're so goddamned frightened because suddenly I've decided to say something. Well, let me tell you why I am. Because I want you to know how it hurts when you say things. I want you to know that saying things hurts people. But secrets are safe. They're harmless."

"That's not true!" Barbara screams at Louisa. "You hate secrets just as much as you hate talking because you hate everything!" The air jumps. "You can't stand to have things out in the open only because if everything ever came out you'd find out how much you hate everything! How you hate us! You said so yourself. You hate us, you always hated us."

"Oh, no," Louisa says, shaking. "I'm not afraid. Because inside I don't hate. It's you that hates inside, so deep inside that you never get to it, you've got so many of your precious layers of honesty to get through before you hit bottom. Oh, no, it's not me that hates everything, it's you—"

"We cannot stand it," Sadie is sobbing. "We can't stand it anymore. Please, stop, we hurt. Please, please stop! She can't bear it anymore. She can't bear all this hate."

Simultaneously Barbara and Louisa stop. Sadie is talking about someone else. Louisa looks at Barbara, then turns quickly to Sadie who is wailing. "Barbara, do something!" Louisa begs. "Can't you see she's crazy?"

"You," Barbara says. "You try, for once, to do something to help her."

Louisa leans across the table to Sadie, touching her on the edge of her hands, then touching her folded arms, stroking the sleeve of her blouse. "Sadie, get hold of yourself.

Who are you talking about? Stop crying and tell us. We want to hear you. Please, please, stop all this crying and tell us. Who are you talking about, Sadie? We're listening. We're not yelling at each other." Sadie, gradually calming down as she wipes the tears from her face, looks up.

"Who? What?"

"You just said, 'She can't bear all this hate.' Do you mean that you can't bear it? I can't? Barbara can't? Who are you talking about?" Sadie suddenly brightens up and smiles warmly at Louisa.

"But you know. Of course you know who I'm talking about. Who else could I be talking about?" Barbara and Louisa now exchange looks. Barbara sits down and puts her hand on Sadie's shoulder.

"Sadie, honey, just tell us who you mean."

Lightly Sadie says to both of them, "Mother."

The two older sisters shiver. Sadie continues, "That's the whole point of everything! That's what I've been trying to say ever since it happened. It was Mother."

"It was Mother what?" Barbara asks, almost too exhausted to speak.

"It was Mother who did it," Sadie says.

Louisa looks at Sadie in total horror. The only possible explanation is that Sadie hallucinated, taking her hands to her own throat, thinking it was Mother. "Sadie," Louisa says, gently but unable to conceal her own fear, "Sadie, is that what was so clear? That Mother was—was there?"

"No, no, you don't understand!" Sadie looks at both of them, warmly smiling. "What was so clear was that you hated me. That was what was clear. And that's when it happened."

"Oh, God," Barbara says. "Sadie, please. Please, now, tell me what happened. It isn't clear at all."

"Well," Sadie cups her hands in her lap and sits up. "I

started to hurt because you were hating me so much, and everyone was hating everyone, I guess, so I started to hurt thinking of how everyone was hating each other, and it kept on hurting and then I screamed because—because. I don't know why I screamed. I guess it was because it was the only thing I could do. I was frightened."

"Of yourself?" Louisa asks.

"Sort of," says Sadie, bewildered. "I mean, yes and no."

Barbara now speaks. "Sadie, did you take your own hands to your own throat? That's all I want to know."

Sadie covers her mouth with her hands, then, alarmed, pulls them away. "Did I? I don't know. Did I?"

Barbara looks at Louisa and, at last, she breaks down. Leaning back in her chair she lets the tears drip onto her lap. There is no answer. Sadie leans over, glad to cheer Barbara up.

"Don't cry, Barbara, don't cry. It's all over now. Everything's all right. You see, she's made everything all right."

"Mother?" Louisa asks, still unable to piece Sadie's explanation into any coherent picture.

"Yes, Mother. She takes care of everything. Now, how silly," Sadie says, "that you're crying like that, Barbara. Come on. She's here and it's all okay."

Louisa gets hold of herself. "Sadie, do you realize how you're talking? I mean, do you have any idea of what it sounds like?"

"Of course, Looza. I've been trying to tell you all night that I do know. I know myself much better than you ever thought I did. That's what I've been trying to get across to both of you all night. And oh, my goodness, it's been all night, too!" Sadie looks out of the window. "Look, Looza, Barbara. Look, the sun is rising! And we didn't even notice it!" Barbara looks up at the small kitchen window, her tears blurring her vision. Her eyes ache with salt and fatigue. She is utterly spent. So is Louisa. But Sadie jumps up, happy that the sun is rising and it's going to be a beautiful day.

"Look, isn't it beautiful? Oh, my goodness, look how it snowed. I've never seen so much snow in Washington." Sadie opens the window with her short fluffy arms, billowing as the cold air streams in.

"Brrrrrr," Louisa dramatizes, smiling faintly. "It's cold!"

Barbara rubs her shoulders; but the cold feels good for a second. "That's enough, Sadie. Now, close it." Sadie obediently shuts the window, a little out of breath when she turns to them.

She pats her stomach. "I'm getting so fat! I shouldn't have eaten all that ice cream," she purses her lips. At this moment she looks like a cuddly doll. Both Louisa and Barbara want to embrace her and rock her in their arms to the sound of the loon's cry in the children's woods. The sun now rises, fanning the sky in cold light-feathers. Sadie stands, her eyes glimmering, in front of the window, the sun a red circle behind her. "You see?" Sadie says. "The sun is rising and we're all awake and everything is just how it was supposed to be."

Louisa and Barbara nod incomprehensibly, waiting for the first night to give itself over to the second day. "You see?" Sadie says to both of them. "She's here all the time and she won't let us hate each other. She loves us. I love you." Sadie kisses both her sisters warmly. "Now," she says, cheerfully. "Let's all go to sleep for a little while and then we'll have a nice breakfast together and begin on the second floor. Okay?"

They all leave the kitchen. But as Louisa leads them out of the kitchen, she walks out the pantry and the dining room through the living room, avoiding till the last possible moment the portrait. They reach it; Louisa hurries up the stairs.

Barbara has as little desire to see it as she does. Only Sadie pauses, a brief second on her way upstairs to bed.

The portrait hangs dead still. Sadie shakes her tired head, wondering how everything could be so different and so exactly the same.

❧ SECOND FLOOR ❧

IN THE BEDS
THEY HAD AS CHILDREN

ON THE THIRD FLOOR, THE DOORS OF EACH BEDROOM—DOLL size—are shut. Silence. Curtains are drawn, shades pulled down, to block out the morning light beginning to spread over the house. Each daughter undresses and then crawls into her bed, the bed she slept in as a child, welcoming, at first, the wonder of her privacy.

Then, unable to sleep, in turn Barbara, Louisa and Sadie find childhood preserved in the globes, cones, and bars of each bed.

Barbara: A three-quarter bed of maple, the color of syrup, with rounded bedposts like small globes, four worlds, one at each corner. She remembers lying in bed waiting for her father to come in and tell her a story, wondering which bedpost, which world, he would tell her a story about that night.

Her father had been over the entire world, following an important person in the government who was almost the

161

President, but not quite. He could tell her about places with names that would lull her to sleep when he left: New Delhi, Pakistan, a world called Indochina—that was one bedpost. Paris, Rome, the Continent, another. And one called Russia that was larger than all of the others (in her mind) and where it was always cold and people wore furs. The last bedpost was Home. Every night Barbara hoped that he would reach the bedpost called Home, with the lamp beside it lighting up the wood sweet. She would wait for the end of Da's story, his kiss, and the light off, knowing that she was Home, safe, lying in the dark thinking, Pakistan, New Delhi, Paris Rome and Russia where it is always cold.

But there were many nights when Da did not come in and tell her a story. He was away. She would look at the bedposts, trying to remember which was which, only knowing Home, trying to remember so that she could bring her father back to her room. If only she could remember which world he was in. She would look at the two maple globes at the foot of her bed, afraid to turn off her light, wondering where Da was, and when would he come Home? She wanted to go all over the world with him, from bedpost to bedpost, in one of his stories. But Da didn't come in. Nurse came in; did not tell her a story; turned off the light; told her to sleep.

In the dark Barbara imagined the worlds, wondering if it were dark where Da was, because he told her that time changed. Time changed in different places but it was always the same at Home. It might be daytime where Da was, and why couldn't he be Home where it was dark? And maybe he was in Russia, and cold. Or New Delhi, and hot. Was he warm in the sun? Or was it snowing all over?

Barbara now recalls her childhood room, and, opening her eyes, she expects to see the large window with yellow curtains where she would stand, sometimes, looking out over the large slope of the backyard, wondering if Da would be Home. But she sees a wall. This is not the room where she slept as a child. It is a tiny guest room. She wants the window; the hope at the window. And then Barbara remembers, once, a vision she saw outside that other window, in her room, one night.

It was snowing all over. Mother had told them to go to bed and not to expect Da home because of the snow. Nurse ushered them upstairs. The light was turned off. Barbara had waited until Nurse left; waited until she knew that her sisters had been tucked in and Nurse had gone to her room. Then, quietly, she got out of bed and went to the window.

She touched the glass; cold. Wiping the windowpane clear, she gazed out over the white slope, waiting. The snow stopped, and the moon rose pure in the night sky. She looked at the moon, the world farthest away, a white globe, and wondered if the moon were cold and hard like glass. And then, she saw something moving over the snow. Small, human, it seemed to glide over the snow magically, she couldn't believe it, it was her father, it was Da walking on snow, above the snow, and she thought, He's Home, Home, it is Da walking on snow coming Home.

She rushed from the window and climbed into bed, waiting for Da to come in and kiss her good night. She heard the door downstairs open. Soon. Any minute now.

But then she heard Mother's voice, and some noises; then, nothing. She thought she heard them going down the hall, quietly.

Barbara now turns in the bed, and realizes that she has been lying off to one side; as if her husband were sleeping beside her. But she is alone. The bed seems to her as large as it seemed when she was a little girl, large as the lake in summer. Cautious, she moves under the sheets, unable to believe that Tom won't come into the room in a moment and get into bed beside her, kiss her good night and turn off the light.

She thinks it must be snowing in Michigan.

Louisa: A three-quarter bed of maple, darker than Barbara's, with conical bedposts. She remembers lying in bed and, unable to sleep, running her fingers over the headboard, feeling how smooth and flat it was; then running her fingers over the grooves and ridges of the post nearest her head where she could not sleep. If any light were in the room she stayed awake. Some nights she would get out of bed and put the extra blanket under the door to block out the hall light. Then she would get back into bed, and think, It's a forest. The bedposts are trees. The blanket the ground. And I'm under the ground where it is darkest because that is the only place I can sleep, the only place where there is no light and no voices.

Louisa now lies in this bed, the room as dark as possible, but not dark enough. The silence, however, is a blessing. On either side of her room Sadie and Barbara are quiet. Quieter than it was when she was little and had to crawl all the way under the covers not to hear the sounds next door. She closes her eyes, wanting to sleep. But, just as it used to happen when she was a child, she sees small starbursts of different colors underneath her eyelids. She shuts her eyes tighter, hoping that the colors will disappear.

Then she remembers that when she was little she was afraid that her eyes might not open in the morning. They would be glued shut, she thought. I'll wake up blind. The world will be forever dark, and I won't be scolded by Nurse in the morning for putting a blanket under the door because there will never be any light to keep me awake. She remembers thinking that if she were blind she would imagine the whole world as a forest with smooth trees and flat places like the headboard, or grooved and ridged like the bedpost. It would be too scary if the world did not feel like her own bed at night. And then she would wonder if voices would be louder or softer if you were blind. She would realize that they would be louder.

And then she would start hearing things. She would try not to listen, but she still heard them. The noises were coming from next door, in the room next to hers, her parents' room. She heard her mother's and her father's voices and wished harder than before that she were in a forest.

Why did they speak at night like that? They never spoke that way during the day. She could never hear the words, only the way they sounded.

She lies now, flat on her back, testing the silence. It is there. No voices.

Now she remembers that when she was very small she used to share her room with Barbara. She doesn't remember when or why she was moved to the room next to her parents; but she does remember her bed was taken out and that in her new room it looked lonely. The new room felt like the wrong room to her, her bed in the wrong place, and whenever she tried to sleep she thought that someone was missing. Until she heard the voices next door. And then she wouldn't know what she wanted, silence or voices, solitude or company.

She turns on her side. Her head brushes against the flat smooth headboard. Her arm reaches out to meet Patrick's hair with her fingers. It reaches nothing.

He's not there. Silence.

And suddenly Louisa thinks it would be scary to sleep alone every night in a silent bed and not feel his hair.

Sadie: A single brass bed with shimmering bars, the head-board the lines of a gilded cage. Already lying in bed, feeling the familiar softness of the mattress, Sadie also feels how she sinks down into it, and doesn't float as she felt she floated when she was light and little. The old linen sheets she put on the bed feel thick and smell of Mother's linen closet. She lies there, breathing deeply, all of the words out of her. She is restful.

But then words come back to her, the prayer she recited every night at the side of the brass bed. She doesn't say prayers out loud any more. Sometimes she prays silently to herself in bed, little prayers about her family. She tries to recall the scene of her childhood prayers. The scene comes back to her in pieces: Nightgown. A little blond girl. The room all blue, Madonna blue. The edge of the bed just at her eyes. The blanket tickling her nose when she bowed her head. Her palms flat, together, sticky. And out of the corner of her eye the light of the brass bars, golden. She would keep her eye on the brass bars loving them because she had the best bed, the only bed that shone. (The others had wooden beds and even if they were bigger they weren't half as nice as her bed which was smallest because she was the youngest and just her size.)

Then, the door would open. Quickly she would close her eyes and begin, "Now I lay me down to sleep, I pray the Lord my soul to keep," loud and clear. Then she would stop. Mother would enter the room and stand at the foot of the bed, waiting. Sadie would take deep breaths, trying; but she couldn't say the next words. She would keep her eyes shut tight, and then open them, see her mother, quickly look at the brass bars, and then try again. But she couldn't.

Then Mother would say, "And if I die," and Sadie would quickly finish, "before I wake I pray the Lord my soul to take Amen."

"Amen?"

"Amen."

"So soon?"

"And bless Mother and Da and Barbara and Looza and Jewel and everyone Amen."

"You left out Nurse."

"And Nurse. Amen?"

"Amen. Now get into bed."

Sadie now tries to imagine what it looked like to her mother: the little girl who said her prayers even though she wasn't told she had to, but did, and was made to finish them correctly. Did the room look tiny and the bed huge to her mother? Did Mother see how the light glittered on the bars?

Sadie would get up into bed and under the covers alone, looking at her mother standing at the foot of the bed on the other side of the one brass bar. Mother said Good night, and on her way out she would turn off the ceiling light with a switch, leaving Sadie alone in the dark.

It was then—alone in the dark—that Sadie would hold onto the image of the light on the bars, imagining that they still glowed in the dark room lighting up behind her. She never turned to look. She just said to herself over and over again, They shine, they shine, they shine.

Now, Sadie reaches out and touches one of them. It is cold. She draws her hand back. Why couldn't she ever say, "And if I die?" Mother always had to say it for her.

And now Mother can't say it for her because she has died. Sadie sighs, pulling the linen sheets around her shoulders.

She looks at the single bar across the foot of the bed, dull in the faint light coming from the window. The bar is close to her. When she was little it seemed miles away, and Mother on the other side of it even farther, farther than she could reach. But now Sadie barely fits into the bed. The bars wedge her in. They do not shine.

"Now I lay me down to sleep," Sadie murmurs, "to sleep, and, and, Pray the Lord her soul to keep, yes, her soul, to keep, to keep for me to take Amen?"

THE
DEATH PAPERS

SADIE TOSSES HER HEAD, THE HAIR FLYING AROUND IN CURLING blond wisps, falling as the sunlight falls into the room. The noise of buses and truck engines carries over across the back garden and up into her room from a main Washington thoroughfare winding around the back of the house. Purged from the dark of the night her eyes glance quickly over the bright objects in the guest room, a room so tiny that there is just enough space for a bed, a standing lamp, a small bureau and Sadie's body. Wide awake, she jumps out of bed, her body forced to sit and rise as she dresses. She puts on her new pantsuit and then begins to brush her hair. Feeling that today she must be changed, and that things must be different —good feelings must be restored—she decides to put her hair up. She takes out the bobby pins from her purse; they spill over the wooden floor. Getting down on her hands and knees, she crawls, scraping up the bobby pins into her fist. Suddenly, sitting on her knees, she giggles; then, just as suddenly, the airiness of her giggling contracts in the room, and falls, condensed, into her memory. Oh no, Sadie says to herself. Oh no, none of that today. I have to be mature today. I still have to show my sisters that they have underestimated me. And they have, they really have (she insists as she grunts, rising from the floor). I must try to be serious today—but I'm so happy! And so hungry. She fumbles with her hair and the bobby pins, putting it up in a tangled bun. She then leans close to the mirror; her cheeks are as smooth as mounds of snow, tinted by the sunrise Sadie welcomed long ago. Well (she stands back), I've underestimated myself, too. Then this thought, too serious, floats out the door and into the hallway as Sadie herself drifts through the floors of the house, down to fix breakfast.

She stops at the door of her father's bedroom on the second floor, which is near to the corner of the stairs. The second floor, in contrast to the third, appears to be a paradigm of organization; nothing there seems out of place. Her father's bedroom is bare; the morning light falls pale through the semi-transparent curtains. She shivers. Her father lying in bed (she does not want to think of this, moves) was dwarfed by the size of his bedroom, also his library. On the windowsills and in orderly stacks along the walls are the volumes of the Luskin Records. All along the side wall, which Sadie, standing in the doorway, sees directly to her right, are the books that had been moved gradually from the downstairs to Da's bedroom which he never (Sadie refuses to continue thinking). Turning, she sees in a blur his empty desk, the bay window, the gray rug. She leaves. The room, though the sun shines into it, dampens light, the curtains fog the sun and the humidity of his years of asthma still hangs in the air.

She walks past her mother's bedrom, which the sun has not yet reached; then she passes the dark alcove of the study, and turns the corner down the stairs. Looking up, ready to smile, she freezes on the landing. The entire first floor is stained with red, blue and yellow markers on every piece of furniture, haphazard, diagonal, uneven lines destroying the beauty of Mother's things. She wants to rip every single piece of tape off to restore the house to its original luster and proportion. But the daughters have left their marks on everything. She wanders through the living room and then into the dining room, tracing the line of the sun. Everything is taped. She looks up at the chandelier, which bounces rainbows off its prisms onto the walls; rainbows of pink and blue and yellow, in paler patterns of colors like the strips of tape. Sadie is relieved; the rainbows are beautiful. Then, just as she is about to go into the kitchen, she sees in the thin long window in the corner of the dining room a plant. "Oh, how perfectly lovely," she breathes out as she slowly walks over to it. The gardenia is in full bloom, a perfect circle of vanilla folds. Sadie takes the flower in her hands and rips it from its stem, carrying it with her into the kitchen, raising the white petals to her lips and breathing its fragrance. "There," she smiles, placing it in the center of the kitchen table in a glass jar.

She turns to the sink and quietly fixes herself the hot chocolate she has been thinking of since she awoke. Sipping the steaming cocoa she stares at the gardenia. As she looks at its perfect whiteness, content, she remembers her own family, wondering what they are doing. It's Saturday; no one is awake yet. But then Sadie remembers that it is later than it should be, and they must all be out of the house busy with their own things. Maggie and Mark are probably moving into their apartment—George is probably helping them. She sets her cup of cocoa down and scowls. She cannot remember telling George that she would be spending the weekend at

Mother's. But I must have. And even if I didn't, he'll figure
it out. What difference does it make? She returns to the
flower; its petals unfolding from the center in a maze of
creamy sheaths. Sadie feels the crawling baby laughing out
of her; and it disappears. What is she now? A young girl,
dreaming of a flower—a young girl? A virgin. For this moment, this flower resting motionless in the vase in the center
of the table deceives her wonderfully, the perfect blossomed
fragrance. She can wait, she thinks, indefinitely before it
fades, fades.

Barbara opens her eyes. The sun stuffs the room on the
third floor with bright heat. Throwing off the covers, she
sits up, and instantly in her limbs the ache of exhaustion tells
Barbara that she did not sleep well. Remembering more in
its muscles than she remembers in her mind the events of
last night, her body moves with difficulty out of bed. She
takes a deep breath.

Barbara catches sight of the dirty clothes across the back
of the chair. Her one good dress, brought out of habit, hangs
shapeless yellow on the closet door. She stretches and rises
from the bed, walking slowly to her suitcase where she stands,
indecisive. She feels as though she has already gone beyond
the limits of her physical energy, and the sensation, dimly
recalled in her toned-down motion, not like her usual brisk
morning movements, of wanting to give up, of giving up,
now does bring to her mind the events of the night before.
Her mind, half-asleep, forgets its determination to forget,
and listens to the warning dullness of her body that this day
will not and cannot be like yesterday. But I know where I
am. I know exactly what we are to be grabbing today. Preoccupied, with her appearance, what clothes she shall put
on today, she thinks of Louisa's uninterrupted show of good

taste, suspecting that today she will descend the stairs in a new set of tweeds, draped in a long bulky sweater. Barbara wishes that her own clothes were more interesting and less sensible. But at the same time she wishes that it made no difference how she appeared today to her sisters. Only it does; Barbara wants to make an impression, though what kind? She puts on a robe and leaves to take a shower, postponing the decision, angry at herself that she should suddenly care about her appearance at all.

But the face in the bathroom mirror only increases her desire to impress. Her face is dry; she needs some cream. Or maybe some makeup—just a little—to cover up the lines. I look old today. A hot shower should brighten me up. She turns on the shower full, waits for it to warm up, then steps in. The hot water instantly shoots out over her old body, still in good shape, glistening and coloring a young-pink in the steam.

Louisa lies in her bed with her eyes closed, listening to the sound of the shower and trying to get herself out of bed. Her mind is filled with recollections of last night as the warmth of the air in the room gradually penetrates her form with life. But turning over and lazily putting her feet to the floor, the images disappear into the patches of sun on the wood, and she forgets what happened as she begins to dress. Dressing is, for Louisa, a major occupation, requiring not less than an hour to put on the layers of clothes and then the layers of makeup, the undercover and overgloss. This morning she dresses as quickly as possible, not wanting to spend time on her body, naked, but hurrying to cover it up. She does not want to be the last one downstairs—or so she thinks. The moment last night when she left her mother's portrait behind her and stopped, sterile, in the hallway, comes back to her as she dresses and that memory opens up onto the other memory of stealing the diary. In the middle of putting on her eye makeup she stops and goes over to the bedside table, opens the drawer, and takes out the diary. Simultaneously the shower stops; footsteps can be heard in the hall. There is a knock on her door, and then another knock.

"Looza?" says Sadie from the other side. "You awake?"

Louisa quickly puts the diary back. "Yes, yes, come in."

Sadie enters, smiling, dressed in a hideous, to Louisa's taste, lavender knit pantsuit. "I've never seen you with your hair up," Louisa remarks, moving over to continue putting on her eye makeup.

"Oh, dear, don't you look funny!" Sadie says, sitting on the edge of the bed, just like the little sister she is, watching her grown-up sister dressing her face. "I mean, with your eyes one done and the other not done."

"Just a minute and I'll look perfectly normal," Louisa says, friendly. "How long have you been up?"

"Oh, I don't know. The coffee is brewing downstairs. How can you wear all that stuff on your face?"

"It's more like How can I not wear it. I feel naked without it." Louisa takes out a bottle of a new product and gently brushes her cheeks with it.

"I've just never been able to wear makeup properly. I mean, I guess I just don't know how to put it on properly."

"Want me to show you?" Sadie gets up and stands next to her sister. "Here," Louisa says, "this stuff can go onto any kind of complexion, it changes for each person. Let me just dab a little there . . ."

"Really? How remarkable!" Sadie says, letting Louisa put some of the color onto her face. "I thought that you had to buy exactly the right color or you looked funny."

"No," Louisa explains, with sophistication. "They do make that kind of makeup still, but this company puts out the best things. There. Sadie, look at yourself. You look lovely."

Sadie leans toward the mirror and looks at her face, glowing all over with a faint pink light. She laughs a little, embarrassed. "Oh, I like it. It feels sort of funny, but it does look nice, doesn't it? What's it called?"

Louisa hands her the bottle. " 'Translucence.' It's made for you, really."

"I'll have to get some." Louisa looks at Sadie's reflection in the mirror. Her sister looks lovely, but her hair isn't right.

"Sadie, since we've gone this far, why don't you let me do your hair up properly. Okay?"

"This is fun, isn't it?" Sadie smiles as Louisa takes out the bobby pins and begins to brush Sadie's blond curls.

"You've got beautiful hair, you know. How is it so thick and blond?"

Sadie blushes. "I have a confession to make." She watches her transformation in the mirror under Louisa's hands. "I dye it."

"You don't!" Louisa pushes the bobby pins into the mound of hair.

"Oh, but it was so terrible. About a year ago I noticed that it started to go white or gray or something at the roots. And it just frightened me to death. I thought I was turning old and couldn't stand it, so I rushed off to the beauty parlor and told them to do something." Sadie brushes a strand from her cheek as Louisa finishes the last touches.

"Well, they did a good job. It looks perfectly natural."

"Oh, does it? Thank goodness. I wouldn't want anyone to know."

"But, Sadie," Louisa says, taking the brush quickly over her own short hair and flouncing it into place. "Everyone dyes their hair."

"Do you?" Sadie turns.

"Of course. I started going gray years ago, prematurely. I've dyed it for ages."

"Really?" Both Sadie and Louisa turn to the door, where Barbara is standing. "I didn't know that you both dyed your hair." She is in a skirt and sweater, her hair still wet and pulled back severely from her face. She looks even older this way than before the shower, but at least her skin looks fresh and healthy.

"You look like you had a wonderful sleep," Sadie says, smiling.

"Yes. Wonderful. Sound as a log."

The daughters descend the stairs, commenting on each other's appearance, all of them satisfied: Barbara satisfied that she, the eldest, doesn't have to dye her hair. Sadie, satisfied that no one can tell that she dyes hers. And Louisa, satisfied with her own appearance and quite proud of her job with Sadie's.

As they reach the landing on the second floor, Sadie leads them quickly through the hall. But both Barbara and Louisa have a wish to stop and look, to pause and fix this moment before division and confusion. Yet they do not; they resist the temptation to look around, feeling, both of them, that they should know the contents of the second floor, its things, its spaces by heart. Not until they reach the first floor do they realize what will happen today. Just as Sadie was shocked by the disarray of tapes, the violating markings, Barbara and Louisa turn with disgust back toward the kitchen.

"Isn't it awful?" Sadie says. "I was horrified when I came down earlier. I wanted to rip all the tapes off."

"I almost wish you had," Louisa says, reaching for the first cigarette of the morning.

"Thank God you didn't," Barbara says. "We'd only have to go through the whole thing again. I don't think I could possibly remember," she says when they reach the kitchen, "what belonged to me and what belonged to the two of you."

"Oh," Louisa exclaims, seeing the gardenia. "How nice."

"Isn't it?" Sadie beams, rushing over to the cabinet to take out coffee cups. "It just bloomed this morning."

"How could it possibly have bloomed now?" Barbara asks. There is a pause, angry, from her younger sister. "Well," Barbara says, by way of apology, "it is beautiful."

They sit, politely, assuming a defense of courtesy as they sit around the flower. A quiet descends during breakfast, which no one interrupts. All wish to be peaceful and friendly, as if to undo last night's confusion.

But the daughters must move forward, rising into another dimension, bound and printed, closed to the sun, stacked away from the outside light now high and sticking its beads onto the glittering snow. The dimension of the Luskin Records, The Family history, a selected world of indelible sentences recording birth, death, love and the disappearance of love, yellowing in the dark of shelves and fading in the bedroom corners, marks the boundaries of the second floor. There is furniture to be grabbed; but each item—a desk, a lamp, a table, bookends—appears only as another sheaf.

They enter the upstairs study, forgetting until they are all seated with the inventories on their laps, new rolls of tape beside each of them, and Louisa with her everpresent cigarette, that this dark curtained room doubled as their father's convalescence room, doubled continually, for he never convalesced. In an effort to dispel the collective memory of last visits, Barbara stands and plays with the curtains, trying to pull them open. "It's hot in here," she says, as the curtains refuse to let in any light.

"I feel a little cold," Sadie says. "The room reminds me—"

"Let's not talk about it, okay?" Barbara says, still wrestling with the curtains. "I can't see a thing in here, anyway."

Sadie turns on the light beside her. Determined to follow through with her resolution, her new manner, she clears her throat, unaware that she is imitating Barbara's self-importance, and says, "I think that this is light enough. And anyway, the curtains haven't been opened since Da died. Mother never, absolutely never, used this room."

The curtains reply by not moving. The memory shuts them in. The memory of their father cannot be transformed by childhood or softened with a salve of mature acceptance of his deathlike life. *The story of medicine prescribed and medicine taken . . . The story of twenty years in bed . . .* Da's gentleness and soft-spoken manner had gradually disintegrated like his muscles and sagged like his flesh into sickness and then it sunk with his body of bones as soft and malleable as the flesh that hung off them, to death. He volunteered over ten years ago to be a guinea pig for an experimental drug. A chronic asthmatic with other vague symptoms never explained to his daughters, he had passively accepted any ministrations of doctors, nurses, and the devoted attention of his wife. When she married him, she had no idea that her marriage would turn her into a full-time nurse and secretary; but with her typical "strength of character" and sense of duty she painstakingly cared for her husband, as a good wife should.

The daughters remember that he was always short of

breath; used a humidifier in his room; and the nurse kept his room cool. Any approach of the subject with Mother only produced: "Privacy is the special privilege of the sick." Now, the memory of their father lying in bed and gradually flattening in between the sheets and disappearing into the bed and finally being buried in a jar in the ground also brings to their mind a rising, growing curiosity about his lifelike death. The little golden boy, the editor, and the lakeside storyteller merge into the one supine image of old age not even approaching but wrapped in a shroud, kept at a cool temperature, always contained between the sheets and bedcovers by death which did not wait, but hung and hangs, now, in the air of the room.

Barbara sits, trying to fight the stagnation by urging them to get on with the grab. But both her sisters resist.

"I remember," says Sadie, "the last time I visited Da."

"Please, Sadie, don't," Barbara asks.

"I think," Sadie continues, "we should talk about it. That is, after all, what I learned last night. I learned that one has to talk about life, how it feels inside." But she speaks with an outer layer, newly acquired, and not from the inside. She merely gives lip service to a discovery she imagines she has made.

"Did you have to bring that up? I was hoping that we would forget the whole thing."

"Barbara," Sadie says, turning her head gracefully, without flutter. "To forget the whole thing, as you put it, would be impossible. At least, it would be impossible for me. I don't wish to discuss it at length; we did enough of that last night. But I do feel that I should let you know that I've made up my mind today to be entirely myself," she finishes, sounding exactly like Barbara.

"Congratulations," Barbara says, sarcastically, ridiculing

though she does not realize it, her own way of speaking. "Congratulations on your newfound self."

"And I also think," Sadie flourishes, "that you've been sarcastic enough. It's cruel, to all of us. It's most of all cruel to her." Sadie turns to Louisa for support, but the expression on Louisa's face is only a register of confusion. Louisa, observing the uncharacteristic behavior of Sadie, has been trying to form a connection between the Sadie of this morning and the Sadie of last night; but Sadie's phrase, "last time I visited," has planted into Louisa's mind the germ of an image. The germ spreads, confusing her. *Did I ever visit Da in the hospital? I can't remember. I can see him; but then I can't. He fades out. It was Mother I visited, Mother in the hospital before she died, Mother dying and I was with her. Just me.*

"For God's sake," Barbara says, "Mother is dead, Sadie." She calms to repeat, evenly, "Mother is dead."

"Not really," Sadie says, and stops. There is a long silence. Louisa struggles to recover herself, but she cannot stop thinking of the last time she saw Mother; she wants to remember something clearly, it feels important, but she can't with her two sisters there, and the memory of Da's death intruding. It then occurs to Barbara that there is a good way of destroying Sadie's argument, indirectly. She half hopes that Louisa will snap out of it and try to join in her strategy. But, looking over at Louisa, she realizes that Louisa has drifted off. So, Barbara turns to Sadie and in a loud voice, as if to attract Louisa's attention, she addresses Sadie in the authoritative tone that usually works with her youngest sister.

"Why don't we talk a little bit about Da? It might make all of us feel better. Tell us about the last time you visited him."

"Louisa doesn't want to hear it," Sadie says, looking over at Louisa who has forgotten to put her cigarette out.

"What? I don't want to hear what?" Louisa murmurs, trying to get herself back into this scene outside of her. "What don't I want to hear?"

"About the last time I visited Da. You don't want to hear about it, do you?" Sadie sits back, and brushes the wisp of hair which keeps falling over her cheek.

"No, I want to hear it very much. Very much. I can't tell you how much I want to hear it." Louisa now notices her cigarette, and uses it to light another.

"Well," Sadie begins. "The last time I visited—"

"Did you ever visit him in the hospital?" Louisa suddenly interrupts. "Was Da ever hospitalized for anything?"

"No," Sadie says, scowling, returning to her former animation. "No, I don't think he was ever hospitalized. Do you remember, Barbara?"

"In the hospital? No, I don't think so."

"Wait, wait. You must be thinking about the time he—"

"Yes, yes," Barbara now interrupts. "You must be thinking about the time he had that accident."

"What accident?" Louisa asks.

"When he fell down the stairs, you know, that summer at the lake when he fell down the stairs? You remember," *running in from the hall and seeing Da at the top of the stairs and knowing that he was going to fall and trying to run Did I try to run? I was dizzy, everything was I was He was falling and I wasn't there to save him because I stopped, yes, I stopped, because my husband was just coming in on the boat and I ran the other direction to meet him and left Da there falling, he fell*

"When he fell and broke his hip," Sadie finishes for Barbara.

"And he was hospitalized, then, for his hip?" Louisa asks.

"Yes," Sadie says. "My, you're slow today."

"Am I?"

"Yes. But that's beside the point. I'm trying to tell a story and I keep on getting interrupted."

"Didn't that accident put him to bed for—?" Barbara asks, trying now to fight the resurfacing memory.

"Well," Sadie says, "not forever. Only, I guess it really was forever, since he never got up again."

"No, he never got up again," Barbara says uncomfortably. She has now quite forgotten the reason she prompted Sadie to speak of the story which is never going to be told.

"What did he have, anyway?" Louisa asks.

"Asthma, of course," Sadie answers pertly. She is pleased to have all of the answers today.

"No, no," Louisa says. "I mean, he must have had something else. One doesn't die of asthma."

"Well, I never really knew," Sadie says, getting up from her chair. "But we could always look at the records he kept." She goes over to the corner, where the rolltop desk is, and opening the bottom drawer rummages through some loose papers till she finds the folder she is looking for.

"What's that?" Barbara says, leaning to look over at Sadie, whose back is turned while she flips through the pages of a large manila folder.

"It's Da's record," she replies as she turns. "Of all the medicines he took. It isn't the original. The doctors took the original. It's just the copy." She moves over to the couch and sits, still looking in the pages as if for something specific. But all she sees are endless timetables with amounts of pills and the names of drugs listed on them. She looks at the pages which note, by an agreed number code, how well he feels, what his reactions are to the pills, what his activity was that day; never anything more strenuous than walking a few steps, or at the very most, being wheeled outside in the spring to look at the "young people," as he put it. In the midst of these timetables penciled observations are haphazardly thrown in, hard to find in the general mass of detailed medical information. In their own way, the papers are extraordinary. The meticulous newspaperman made an excellent guinea pig.

"Let me see," Barbara says, sitting next to Sadie on the couch. They spread the folder between their two laps. Louisa remains in her chair.

"Louisa? Looza? Why don't you join us?"

"I don't think we're going to find anything," Barbara says, disappointed. The record is too painful for Barbara, who was closest to her father in the weeks before his death, moving in and living in 1331, waiting it out with Mother. During those weeks, she discovered that what had probably killed her father was the medicine from the experiment. At this moment, sitting with the papers, Barbara does not want to share any of her father with either of them, and feels that the papers belong to her more than to either one of them. But she also feels protective; that their father died because of the side effects of a drug is not something that Barbara feels should be public property, public to the family. Even Mother, Barbara remembers, never forgave the doctors, blaming them, and not Da's willingness to submit, for his death.

When he did die, five years ago, his death merely ended the process of dying with order. The funeral differed only slightly from the years of cold assemblies in this room; it was the last gathering around him. At that assembly, in the church as he requested, Mother appeared annoyed at her sons-in-law, volunteering arms to escort her into the church.

She wanted no escort except the man who was ashes. Then, just at the threshold, Mother clutched Tom's arm. She said nothing. A dark voice read the Twenty-third Psalm to the silent family as Mother stared, dry eyed, at the vase filled with ashes, her only company, now.

Louisa sits thinking of her father, the memory of the funeral coming back to her. It had been strange; Mother wearing a crazy straw hat, a gift that Da had brought back for her from the Orient. And her sons-in-law circling around her like drones. It had been hot. Too hot to cry, with everyone sweating. And Patrick. Yes, Patrick, Louisa remembers, had paid attention only to Mother, as if it were the last chance that he might have to make it up with her, as he was the favorite son-in-law of Da, but least favorite of Mother. Louisa could do nothing. She had sat off to one side, in the waiting room, smoking, wanting Patrick to come over and speak with her. She remembers thinking what a fool he was to think that Mother would soften; she hardened when Da died. Louisa had not cried until later, when she and Patrick had returned to Connecticut, and, that night, she had screamed at him over some trivial misunderstanding, then burst into tears thinking only of her father who was dead and who had loved Patrick. She had not visited him in the hospital. But, thank God, Louisa thinks, thank God he did not know Patrick and I were having problems.

Louisa softens, now, into the chair. She can feel tears starting, but does not know why. She feels the wet on her cheeks, and thinks of sleeping alone.

Sadie and Barbara look up from the papers. Quickly Sadie rushes over to Louisa, wrapping her arms around her. "Looza, Looza, it's all right. Don't cry."

Louisa looks up into Sadie's face. She does not want her sister hugging her. She controls herself. The tears subside, helped by Louisa's desire to get Sadie away from her body.

"It's all right," she says. "I'm fine, Sadie. You don't have to comfort me."

Sadie removes her arms, hurt. "Are you sure, Looza? Are you sure you're all right?"

Louisa nods. "I'm sorry. I didn't mean to lose control of myself like that."

Barbara closes the folder, anxious to hide the papers from Louisa's sight. But she cannot hide them; they are part of the grab. Louisa is still shaken up by what Barbara thinks is the memory of Da.

"Louisa?" Barbara says. "I'm sorry that I started talking about him. I didn't realize that it would upset you so much."

"What?" Louisa looks at Barbara.

"I said, I'm sorry that we started to talk about Da."

"Da? Oh," Louisa lowers her head. "That's right."

"Well," Sadie says, "I think it's only natural to think about Da when we're all sitting here. And poor Da, sick and in bed all the time. It's such a nasty thought."

"You are only making it worse," Barbara says. But she now suspects that Louisa was not crying for their father; but for something else. She wishes that Sadie would shut up, or, better, leave the room.

"But I'm not trying to make it worse, Barb." Sadie sits down. "I'm only saying that it's really sad and that Looza should not be afraid to cry. It's okay to cry. And she never cries. Do you, Looza?"

Louisa makes no answer.

"I mean, I cry all the time. It's just because I can't help it, you know, and it feels good, sometimes."

"Sadie," Barbara says. "Would you please stop it?"

"Oh, I seem to keep on getting you mad at me," Sadie says. "I don't mean to, Barb. I really don't."

Sadie looks from one sister to the other. Something is going on between the two of them that she doesn't like. "What's going on?"

"Nothing," Barbara says. "We're just wasting time." She wants to begin the grab in this room, but something stops her. She feels overprotective of Louisa, and, strangely, tender toward her younger sister. The three of them wait, now, Barbara and Louisa unconsciously approaching each other, and yet they each hesitate on the borders of trust. Louisa looks up at Barbara, wondering if she will make a move. She sees her older sister's healthy face, curious eyes; then she catches sight of Sadie's glowing face, Sadie, who forced the other two together last night, sitting now as a barrier.

They say nothing to each other, Barbara wondering what Louisa is thinking, Louisa wanting to tell her out loud but not with Sadie there. Barbara closes her eyes.

"Let's get going," she says.

First choice falls to Louisa. She pauses; then she says, "Barbara? Would you like the papers?"

Barbara holds them in her lap. "It's your choice, Louisa."

"I know it's my choice. But I'm just asking you."

Barbara looks down at the folder, thinking that this is all that remains of her father, except memories that hurt. But the papers do not hurt; they distance, they codify and explain, at least partially for Barbara, his death. She does not move or speak, however.

Louisa takes Barbara's silence as a sign that Barbara wants the papers but will not admit it. Louisa rises and places a strip of red on the rolltop desk. Then she turns and says, quietly, "Patrick always wanted a rolltop desk."

Barbara looks up at Louisa. It is the first time that Louisa has taken something for her husband. Barbara wonders what the gesture means. She puts a small strip of yellow on the folder, thinking that she will take the time to decipher all of Da's little comments thrown in between the numbers and the medicines. And, when Sadie tags the curtains with blue, carefully counting to see exactly how many there are, Barbara cannot help but smile.

"I don't know why you want those," Sadie says. "What could you possibly want them for?"

"Herself," Louisa says.

Sadie shrugs, thinking how silly it is to take the papers when Barbara could have had the curtains, the best thing in the room.

THE
LOVE LETTERS

THE ORGANIZATION OF THE SECOND FLOOR CONTINUES TO modify and to abort their expectations. They had expected the second floor to be simple, as simple and straightforward as the codified Luskin Records and the titles in the library, lines upon lines of names. But the second floor is a design of doubt. Its narrow hallway is enclosed not by two long walls, but by the images of a man and woman, two ancestral portraits that dominate the dense network of their parents' married life upstairs. Their two bedrooms branch off the hallway like two arms, opening, reaching for each other across the hallway, across the ancestral images, trying to meet where they were meant to meet, at the Luskin Records; but stopping at the trunk of love letters, unopened.

In the hall upstairs, the three wives move toward the Records in their father's bedroom; but hesitate, doubting each other, questioning The Family, wondering how to leave this house and return to husbands after they have grabbed at the pieces inside the rooms of their parents' marriage.

Sadie stands apart, feeling rejected by her two sisters. She did say to herself that she would "behave" today. But other words were caught up into her resolution, words that were part of the Code, part of Mother's entrance into the Luskin Records.

How do you behave when you've lost something? Something that you thought you'd get back? But I know, I know what it is to behave. I know the Code—don't I? I know it better than my sisters. I've lived by it.

But what have I done? I've done one thing and I've called it marriage. I've done another thing and I've called it being a mother, and I've done a lot of different things and called them Family. I have three daughters, one husband, and myself.

But I got something else last night. Didn't I?

She doubts it, as she stands, thinking of her father and of her sisters who are leaving her out, today, ignoring her. She feels that she lost whatever it was that she did get last night, looking at her sisters' backs, turned from her; and seeing the distant gray at the end of the hall that is her father's bedroom. And she wants whatever it was so badly, that she gradually straightens up, fixes her face into a smile, and convinces herself that it makes no difference to her that her two sisters aren't paying attention to her. After all, she does have the Code.

But Love was never dictated by the Code. Sadie has persisted in thinking that a special love existed between her and Mother, bridged by the Code, locked by the Code. All morning, Sadie has felt a rough edge to her fantasy, an abrasion, that now grates in the widening space between her and her sisters, eating away to memories, not fantasies, records, not lyrics of her own marriage. Uneasy, she tries to use the Code for aid, she tries to find her heart fitting into it. But the edge rubs against her. Her heart is too needy to fit to the Code.

Sadie now realizes, against the smile on her face, against the softness of her body, the error in imagining her life to be a large pool of good feelings. Her life is at odds with her heart, now. Her marriage scrapes at it. Her daughters (like her sisters) turn against her. Her husband says he has to work all the time, and can't be at home.

I won't let myself think that way.

But as soon as she rejects her reality, her heart lands upon a sweet (to her) wish. To have married the other one, the one she loved. To have other children, be a different wife. But that other man didn't fit. He could never have lived by the Code. She is torn between the desire to have been a wife who never had to sign a paper saying she would never leave, and the wife she is, who did sign a paper and stamped her marriage with security.

A different wife? But—but isn't the Code the Code whatever I do? Even if I had married against Mother's wishes, the Code would have still locked me into behaving like a Luskin. So what if love isn't—But I want love, to love him and her and them and this and everything. Why doesn't anybody believe me? God, you believe me, don't you? Then why do you make it hurt? It's not supposed to hurt like this. I know it isn't.

The telephone rings. In the background Sadie hears the

run, the exclamation, the return of footsteps, the words, "It's for you, Sadie." She responds with the necessary movements; but her mind is outside of herself, caught in the fabric of an image remaining outside. When she arrives at the telephone, answers, hears her voice, she then identifies the sound: Wife. The voice on the other side: Him. *The other voice makes me wife. Other voices make me sister. Others make me Mother. Mother makes me daughter. Daughter makes me Mother.* But at this moment certain words are required: "Yes, I slept well, did you, honey?"

"Well, now, dahling," George says, as he seems to take a paper in his hand. "I might have slept better if I hadn't been waiting up for you."

Sadie giggles. "Oh, but honey, you knew I was going to stay here at Mother's. I took a suitcase and everything. I told you nearly a week ago that I was planning to be staying here this weekend. Did you think I was coming back? Poor dear, staying up for your little Sadie to come home. I'm sorry," Sadie says.

"Sadie, you did not tell me you were staying. With all this coming and going the past weeks it's hard to tell what you're doing or where you are. It does seem that you are indulging, dahl, and forgetting your family just a little bit." George's mellow voice makes it impossible for him to sound angry, no matter how angry he may feel; and Sadie has taken, throughout the marriage, refuge in the evenness of his voice, never the meaning of his words. Part of signing that paper was promising to listen to the meaning of his words. But Sadie could not; she could only listen to how he said things, never knowing what the "it" was, since she could only respond to the phrase and never "it." Never itself. Never him, himself, but just his voice carrying over into her eyes. That is why talking on the phone is difficult. She cannot use her eyes as she is used to. Well, Sadie thinks, What is it?

"What is it?"

"What is what, dahling?" George asks, "What's happening there, honey? Is everything all right?"

Sadie can respond to this. "Oh, it's just wonderful, George, you can't imagine how wonderful it is. It began with a lovely talk with Looza, you know. But then we got started on the actual grab and everything has been so—so interesting, honey. I don't quite know how to describe it," Sadie falters. Tomorrow or the next day she will be talking with her husband face to face, but she doubts her eyes will be as useful to her as they have been in the past for looking askance, or shining with a blinding blue. She will have to go back to her husband. It is unavoidable. And what then? What will she tell him?

"Describe what, honey? Something happen?"

"Oh, nothing unusual, honey. Nothing unusual." That is a lie. "Well," Sadie begins, feeling as she felt the night before, pressed to say something from the inside. "Something did happen, though I can't possibly explain it over the phone. Why, I really don't know if I can explain it at all." Sadie blushes, ashamed to include him, her husband, the stranger at the threshold, the one who doesn't come home in time for dinner. She was new when she married him. Fresh. That she wasn't new any longer, that her innocence was lost, misplaced, and she couldn't go back to George if she didn't have it with her—that was something that happened. But even that wasn't it—though at this point, beginning to feel frightened, Sadie knows that she is approaching it and the approach is what is frightening her.

"You getting along fine with your sisters?"

"Oh, no—I mean, yes, fine, fine. That's not it at all," Sadie rushes to clarify. "No, what happened has something to do with them, and with us, I think, honey, but now's not the time to talk about it. How are the girls? And have you heard from Maggie and, and—" Sadie cannot remember her daughter's new husband's name.

"The girls are fine. No word from the other marrieds. You going to be back, tonight?"

"Oh, honey, I don't think I can," Sadie coos. "There's so much to do, why, we've barely begun today. And we have to do the house, you know. Absolutely the whole thing." Then, Sadie thinks, I will reach what it is.

"Okay, dahl," George says. "I miss you." Though he says it in exactly the same tone in which he says everything, the words strike Sadie and her heart leaps up, afraid. She wants to ask, Do you? Do you miss me? But then the tone of his voice, delayed, rings in her head, and subdues the almost excited question. It is no wonder that George and Sadie have been able to live together in relative peace for nearly twenty-five years; his voice has been his best shield against her songs. Now Sadie detects a new note in the ringing of her husband's voice, though she cannot name it. She rushes to answer, "But I'll be back soon with all sorts of delicious things."

"Good-bye."

"Good-bye."

Sadie hangs up the phone, thinking over their conversation.

Phrases attach themselves to marriages: "Now's not the time"; "the girls are fine"; "okay, dahl"; "be back soon"; little phrases with large forms looming behind them, phrases superimposed on the forms, the forms of a man and a woman looming larger than the phrases of husband and wife; but looming so large and general against the background that no identification is possible; there is no recognition. One sticks to the phrases (I do I will). For the oversize shadows loom up behind the smaller forms of the husband and wife speaking, nodding, uttering, blinding, behind, unable to be seen, there the man and woman rise and fall in and out of the words of husband and wife, rise and fall in a line of women extending back, accessible here, in the hallway of the second floor.

The three daughters stand, the phone call finished, in front of the leather trunk, below two portraits of ancestors. Barbara, about to name them, does not. Inside the trunk lie the letters of a marriage as it was made into phrases.

"Whose turn is it?" Louisa says. She is afraid that they will, in fact, open the trunk. But the second floor is a floor of confounded exchange, and the hidden exchange of their parents' courtship is but one of the returning interruptions; the phone call, another; Barbara and Louisa's conversation, displaced, another.

"So," Barbara says, now that Sadie is not between them, "you've got second thoughts about the divorce?" She is thinking of Louisa taking the rolltop desk, hoping that it is not meant as a parting gift to Patrick. Divorce—a divorce in the Luskin Family—is intolerable to Barbara. "Patrick is such a fine man," she says.

"Barbara, listen," Louisa says, looking at the rug in the upstairs hallway, and tracing out, absentmindedly, its pattern. "Well, I was going to say that I didn't want to talk about it. But I guess some part of me does; the part of me distracted in there." She indicates the study. Barbara turns her head as if to catch sight of the part of Louisa, wondering, still in there. But it is part of herself caught in there.

Louisa continues: "We didn't—I mean, don't have a perfect marriage. But who does, really? Sometimes it seems to me we don't know each other at all. I wonder if one ever really knows anyone completely. But that doesn't make a

difference, really, when it's your own marriage that you're
wondering about. Because you're not in anyone else's marriage but your own. At least, one can say that it is your
marriage, it belongs to you, and you have the freedom to take
it or leave it. Except, you're not free to leave it. But my
marriage has not been smooth, never as smooth as yours.
That always bothered me, to be honest"—Louisa smiles—
"now that I think about it." Louisa pauses, shifting her
weight from one foot to the other, as if to allow past thoughts
to be confirmed in the present. Together Louisa and Barbara
pause, testing their resistance to the past.

"My marriage isn't perfect."

"But it's always appeared stable. I never imagined,"
Louisa persists, though she has imagined many times and
delighted in the imagining, "you and Tom had any problems."

"We don't." Barbara quickens. "Not problems, not perfect,
either. I think—it's suddenly that I'm thinking differently.
I'm wondering. I've got questions, not problems, questions."

"Like what? You don't have to tell me, if you don't—"

"No, I do. I want to. But I don't know how. It's not really
questions. Sort of a feeling, I guess that I'm not—" With
nothing for her hands to do, she smooths her already smooth
hair. "We're not—maybe he feels it, too. I never thought of
that. We're good friends, you know. Best friends. But we
don't say everything to each other. So maybe he might be
feeling it too (*Him? That straight blond man? The one who
arrives at exactly six, who takes out the sherry at exactly
quarter past? The one who does not ask, Do I want to? Do I
want a drink? But just rolls over and moves closer and, with
the still, direct, and almost motionless motion—I close my
eyes—suddenly he is*) but I doubt it. Not the marriage. No
doubt that (*it is a failure to be so perfectly matched and so*

uncomfortable that close) as far as marriages go *(in and out in and out and I am thinking When will I fall asleep? And when can I run? And where)* it's a success." Barbara takes a deep breath, as if she has been running. "I don't know. I'm not certain where we are going. Yes, yes," she lights up, momentarily a resemblance, then ends as the resemblance falls off: "Yes, I don't know what direction I'm going or whether I can take us there."

She looks to Louisa, who gazes back, inscrutable, just like the gaze of the portrait, her form of resemblance; but then, when she opens her mouth to speak, not the expression of the portrait at all. In the briefest suspension of sound, Mother passes freely in and out of each of them—Mother, or herself, Barbara cannot tell; if, for a split second when the chasm between speaking and not speaking opened wide, Louisa revealed herself to Barbara, she would recognize her no better than she recognizes herself (when she lies in bed and counts the in and out). She begins to see the point of one small phrase Sadie said last night, tacked into Barbara's memory now resurfacing on memory's lip: "Louisa knows herself, you know? From the inside." Barbara wants, now, to ask Louisa, is it true, from the inside? But how, from the inside, when it's not you but she that comes in?

"Is it true?" Barbara says, missing what Louisa has just spoken.

"That marriage doesn't always go someplace? Yes. I think it's true. There isn't always someplace to go that you haven't already been to." Louisa smiles at her difficult phrase. "If you get what I mean. I'm not sure that I do. It just came out that way."

"I get what you mean," Barbara says, watching her sister lean against the banister and light a cigarette. *You mean, sometimes it just lies there, waiting for something to pick up and make it start moving again. Waiting for a rewind. And when that happens, when it's all so still, you just wait; and you're afraid to move even though movement is part of how it is still, unruffled.*

"When did you start to feel anxious about it, Barbara?"

"When? I guess," Barbara bows her head, thinking of waters and skies at odds with the wind, a breathing inside her which by definition should be expired. She lifts her head. "It happened when Mother died." *Till death do us.*

"How funny," Louisa removes the cigarette and folds her arms, thoughtful.

Sadie appears at their side.

"Whose turn is it?" Louisa asks.

Sadie stoops to open the already unlocked trunk of letters. "Oh," Sadie says. "I don't think we should grab these."

"Neither do I," Louisa says.

"I thought we'd just read them." The lid falls against the wall.

"Wait," Barbara says as Sadie reaches in. Inside, just within reach, are the phrases of someone else's marriage. In the uncertainty of marriages now looking on (all voices are the voices that make women wives) an alien, unruly vibration rushes up through their bodies. It quivers, foreign, through their limbs.

The irregular route through the second floor has stopped them, deadlocked, between their parents' bedrooms. Now, a sudden reversal, characteristic of the second floor (all voices are the voices that make wives women), takes them back as they remember, each in turn, the first time they made love with their husbands. The trunk lies open.

These are the letters of the wives.

Sadie: I remember the pillows in the bed, and falling on

them. They were covered with satin and I slipped all over the bed not knowing what to do now that we were married and we had the same bed. I wanted to slip off the bed. I felt like the pillows, puffy, white. I was a virgin. The pillows were fringed with lace just like my wedding veil was fringed with lace and pearls like little moons. There were so many pillows and so much lace and so many layers to get through before he could reach my body and my body just kind of felt like the pillows, it was soft and white and muffled.

I slipped under the sheets. I didn't want him to see me naked. I didn't really think about how being married meant seeing each other naked all over. I'd just thought of kissing, lots and lots of kissing, lips and mouths. I didn't know what would really happen.

It happened under the covers. It was like being ripped. I was ripped open like the pillows and I tried to sing my way through it but it felt like all the little bones of the feathers were pricking me, and then everything went soggy.

We tried it again and again, until it would feel like the feathers were tickling me all over and inside (that's what he said, he said it would feel like that if we just kept at it). So I started to laugh. Just listening to him made me want to laugh, and I thought, he wants me to laugh, so I will, and it was easy to laugh when we got naked because it was so silly to be naked in the same room with a man.

Until I got pregnant. Then it was like having a moon inside of me, getting full, and my body got bigger and bigger, puffed up like a pillow when the bed was made (because the bed was made, we were married and we had moved in), and waited for the moon to push its way out of me.

The moon stared at me, with blue eyes, little specks of night.

Then inside it was night, till another moon puffed me up.

And then another night and moon and eyes.

All that time I didn't scream. I just got softer and softer, and every time a moon popped out I'd make myself sing, muffling the screams with the pillows my body had become, as my breasts got bigger and my belly never got flat again. I just grew into a big giggly pillow.

I started to wear lace again. I remembered I was a virgin when I married.

But I wasn't a virgin. I had already been ripped and shredded. Not by him, but by the need and the lie

I am loved

I am loved shot through me hot and teeming, and I met it with a wave of love, but it tore me apart inside, it tossed my insides around in my head and left a sound there, floating in the night like the loon's laugh. But it was a cry, a baby crying, "Mummy! Mummy! I'm afraid of the dark!"

No one ever came in to turn on the lights. No one ever took the dark away. Ever.

Louisa: His body was different from the others. I could feel his body. Know it. It was as if I'd never really been naked before, as if seeing him naked I could see myself as I was: flat. Boardlike.

But with him I wasn't wooden, I wasn't stiff like I'd been before. I felt like a sapling, I could bend and arc, I could breathe. His hands running over my body, his fingertips gentle, padded, were gentle with me, and I had not expected him to be gentle. But he was, all over my body, and my body felt smooth and glossy.

We lay naked beside each other, his pulse beating against my body, his pulse, my pulse, his, mine, until I felt that my pulse was his and his mine.

But it was strange, too, to lie there naked and not be

ashamed. It wasn't the way I had imagined it. I guess I
thought that only virgins married, and that they were trau-
matized. He did, too. It was funny explaining to him that I
wasn't a virgin (which he knew, anyway). I felt as if I were
disappointing him, because I wasn't innocent, I wasn't fresh.

I couldn't explain to him how he made me feel. How it
was like being made and unmade at the same time, like a
sapling and like polished cherrywood, how he made me feel
warm like being out in the sun and wet like being out in the
rain all at the same time.

And when I began to swell, my skin creaking and small
scratches of stretchmarks appearing, I couldn't explain to him
how I felt. How for the first time in my life I felt full, not
empty, and I was round, not square. I looked in the mirror
at myself, naked, after he had left for work, and I saw a
woman there, and the woman was me. How could he understand that? How can you tell your husband that even though
you weren't a virgin you didn't feel like a woman until he
gave you a child? I didn't trust him with that knowledge. I
couldn't.

He liked the way my arms and legs were little and thin,
like the limbs of a stick figure, but my body was soft and
round in the middle. Being round in the middle was like a
miracle happening to me. But I couldn't tell him those
things.

I gave birth to a son. And then I knew I couldn't tell him.
Thinking of how I had felt like a woman while I was carrying
a boy inside of me.

I looked in the mirror again. Board. Sticks. I looked at my
husband when he came home from work, holding the boy
tight in his arms, afraid that he would drop him. But when I
reached out and held him in my arms, I held him loosely,
wondering how it could be that his pulse had once been mine,

and then he'd been born a boy. He cried. I gave him back to his father.

Then his father gave me another son. And I gave it back to him to hold just as I had the first time. But it hurt the second time. I thought I would die with my tight little narrow hips. I wanted anything, anything to stop the pain, to loosen me up. It went on for hours and hours. Then, it was over. But even before they held him up I knew. I knew it was a boy. It had been so hard giving birth to a boy. And I thought, Is that all I can do? Carry boys around inside of me?

As the boys grew up and walked on their own, I waited for his hands again to run over my body. I waited for his touch, waited for him to give me curves that I didn't really have, trying to convince me that I wasn't getting so thin, wasn't getting brittle and dry. He could convince me, for a moment, that I was soft, and I could feel him on top of me with different male muscles and I reached up for the mountains of his shoulders, climbing.

And then, I would let go, thinking, I never had a daughter. I felt betrayed. He landed on the other side of the bed and fell asleep, not knowing how I felt betrayed. And I couldn't tell him. He was fast asleep.

He always fell asleep afterwards. Even the first time, when I lay there looking at him and thinking, This is my husband. No one else can ever be what he is. He's different from every other man in the world, naked, sleeping.

He's my husband. Husband.

Barbara: The first time it was like the wedding. I wanted to get through it quickly, once the reception was over, so that I would have done everything that I had to do that day. Virgin. Bride. Wife.

Wife stayed. I hadn't counted on it staying the way that it did. I wanted to run.

But he was always there beside me, on every trip we took. Do you want a drink? No, no I don't want a drink. I'm not thirsty like I was thirsty the day we got married.

Being thirsty was the bride, not the wife. Being the wife was counting the in and out, regularly, making sure that everything went the way it was supposed to, which it did. It wasn't good or bad, it was just part of being well matched, looking good together. We did it on schedule, like we did everything else, except that we did it alone, in bed, at night. Only at night. And when we had children, we had to be sure that we wouldn't wake them up, even though we never made any noise when we did it, so we didn't really have to worry.

And the children. My body was a mess. Useless. It was lumpy, misshapen, and I couldn't do anything. I was so heavy with a child inside of me that I couldn't even think about running after a while. I couldn't bend down to touch my toes. And I had to stop bicycling to the grocery store in the seventh month. And I started to walk so funny, with my legs straddling, kind of like a duck walks, not like I walk.

I tried everything, but I finally just had to sit and wait until the child did something. It was born.

But right on schedule another child was born. Perfect symmetry: A boy. A girl.

So then, I sprang back. I got my old form back and I could bend and stretch and I decided not to have any more children because it was good to feel like I could move again, and run.

But the schedule didn't change. I knew that if it was Friday then we would do it, in bed, that night, even though we weren't going to have any more children.

It got so that I stopped thinking about it. We took trips together and we adjusted our schedule to the different time

zones. I remember being disappointed, and I remember sometimes I didn't want to or he didn't want to.

Then. Now, it's different. Now I'm not sure where we are
going. We've already been around the world, and there just
doesn't seem like there's any place to go anymore. Except
backwards. Back to when we first married.

We married each other for love. That was the point. I
know it. I knew it when I realized that being a wife stayed,
day in and day out, because we were married and would stay
married and we loved each other and that was the point of
everything that we did.

But love doesn't have to keep a schedule. And if love
doesn't, then why did we? People have to get places on time.
But love doesn't. It's just there. You don't have to keep track
of it.

So why did I?

I don't know. I don't know about schedules any more.
Maybe there isn't a schedule any more. Maybe that's what
it means when the kids have grown up and left the house
and we don't have to be quiet or pay attention to what time
it is.

Maybe we could even do it in the afternoon.

Maybe that's how we should have done it the first time,
instead of waiting all afternoon until the reception was over
and then waiting until it was dark and turning off all of the
lights.

The letters in the trunk remain untouched.

"I don't think we should read them," Barbara says.

"But why?"

"I just don't think that it would be right."

"But there's nothing wrong with reading them," Sadie says.
"I bet they're just lovely. Don't you want to know?"

"No, I don't," Barbara says.

"Neither do I," Louisa says.

Sadie, however, cannot let them go. She needs them too much. Barbara reaches over to close the lid. Sadie keeps her hands on it.

"But what are we going to do with them if we don't read them?"

"Burn them," Barbara says.

"Burn them! Burn them! But how can you burn them? Those are Mother and Da's love letters to each other. It would be a crime to burn them. How can you even think of burning them?"

"How can you think of reading them?" Louisa says.

"Because—" Sadie says, then stops. Barbara closes the lid, resolved to burn them later that night, against whatever protest Sadie may attempt.

But it is hard for the daughters to burn the phrases of one marriage as it was being made, unsure of the phrases that have made their own marriages. Each of the daughters wonders what it will be like when she finally gets back to her separate home. Their homes seem like foreign countries to them, now; their husbands men they thought they knew, before they opened the trunk of love letters. They are not sure what their husbands' voices will sound like when they meet again, see each other. Or how they will speak to each other at night (if they do speak) after the letters have been burned.

BOOKLINED

BALANCE OF LIBRARY: APPROX. 1500 BOUND VOLUMES. DOES not include miscellaneous books. (See attached sheet of Inventory of 1407). Includes unbound passages, the interpenetration of lines. Location: Bedroom of Mr. P. H. Luskin, "Da, the butterscotch king," in which are sitting his three daughters: Sadie at the edge of his bed, Louisa at his desk, Barbara in his large reading chair. The walls of books surrounding them are their father's territory, a fenced-off area from their mother's rooms. They sit in a triangle.

"It won't work this way."

"What?"

"The grab." The lack of organization. Overexposure. Internal journeys.

"What do we do now?"

"Begin to divide the books. But I think we will have to revise our procedure." Revision: To stick to the subject. To divide the inheritance. "First, we will have to substitute tagging for notations in the inventory. Second, and more im-

portant, we have just got to quit wasting time by talking—"
inside and out.

"I like talking."

"Listen: We have all the time in the world to talk when
this is all over. We have to get this done."

"If we do." Louisa lights a cigarette, thinking as she puts
out the match that she really should quit. The smoke matches
the diaphanous curtains upon which the western light is
fixed. Sadie opens her copy of the inventory, suddenly quiet.
"If we do."

"Whose turn is it?" A tedious drone of books rocks them
in nets of colorless air, their voices like the strands of the
curtains departing from the weave to float in a calm limbo
between female voices and father's books. It is too exhausting
to think, Why is Sadie so quiet? Barbara says this—what does
she mean? Louisa is speaking again, she's excited—what is
she not hiding? Relief: The passages are bound, the books
in order. The names of the books separate their voices for
them. "Know that we have . . ." 33 Volumes of Thackeray,
Pope's translation of Homer, 1806, Milton's Poetical
Works, 1826, 22 Volumes of the Dictionary of American
Biography, 1928 (with Index and Supplement). One title
follows another, modulated by the different tones of the
daughters' voices. They concentrate on the accumulation of
their father's and mother's knowledge, interested in the value
of a few extraordinary books; watching out for the first and
limited editions. Louisa especially devotes her attention to
the books, which mostly belonged to Da. Maybe it's the time
of day—the resentment of the light to give in to the dark;
or the wish (whose?) to hold the night in abeyance—that trans-
forms the daughters into the impersonal titles of his books.
A reverse: the lull of revision, still print and thick binding.

Their father, the newspaper editor, had shared these books

with his wife; but to the daughters, now, the books are a government of the male, rigid unlike any other part of the house. A shift of location: Father governs as they proceed. Vaguely the tedium is punctuated:

"I didn't know he had so many books."

"It's not surprising, really. These weren't just his, you know. A lot of these are from the family collections."

    1 Set—6 Volumes of Ibsen's Plays—*Sadie*
    12 Pepys Diary and Letters—*Louisa*
    3 Audubon and Bachman—Quadrupeds of
        North America—*Barbara*

The sun shifts a notch toward the west as the property changes hands. Sadie, finding the books tedious, looks up and glances over all of the different colors of bindings. Then she turns to her sisters, wondering.

"Whatever happened to Mother's poetry?"

"She burned it," Louisa says.

"No, she didn't," Barbara explains. "Don't you remember? It was in a trunk—a navy trunk—and it sank."

"That was just a story," Louisa says.

"What do you mean, just a story?"

"Well, Mother told me another version."

"When?"

"In the hospital."

"What did she say?" Sadie says. She has always wanted to read her mother's poems, convinced that some of them must be among the books.

"She told me that she had never lost the manuscripts as everyone thought. She burned them, herself."

"But why?" Sadie says, disappointed. "She could have been famous, maybe."

"I don't think she wanted to be famous," Louisa says.

"But what reason could she have had?"

"Maybe just finding out that she was going to die," Barbara says. "That's reason enough for doing just about anything."

"But she burned them years ago," Louisa says. Barbara looks up.

"That's odd," she says.

"Maybe she didn't think the poetry was any good."

"Of course it was good," Sadie says.

"Did you ever read any of it?"

Sadie shakes her head.

"Her standards—"

"Were so high."

7 Audubon's Birds of America—*Sadie*
1 Whitman, Leaves of Grass—*Louisa*
10 Wilson's History of the American People—*Barbara*

Too high. As the daughters continue to grab the books, they begin to remember their parents' marriage, but in a new (fixed) light. None of them has ever understood Mother's contradiction. It is a familiar Luskin story, a story like the story of the poems sinking to the bottom of the sea, which they have passed on to their children without fully understanding it.

Mother arrived in Washington when she was eighteen years old. Stepping out of Union Station, she looked all the way down Constitution Avenue and said, romantically, opening her slim arms, "This is my city." Never graduating from high school, and flouting social conventions, she sought a job as a journalist. By the time she was thirty-one, she had made a successful career as the first woman to be a member of the editorial staff of a newpaper.

Then the war came. The men left for the front. She was

given a post on the *Tribune* left vacant by her future husband, who was later to be Editor-in-Chief.

The Luskin joke, the punchline to the story, was that their
father had to marry their mother to get his job back. And
he did, quite suddenly, marry her. And just as suddenly she
gave up her career.

Mother wrote poetry while the daughters were babies. But
she never pursued the poetry publicly. This was the contradiction that has eluded the daughters: their mother's secre-
tiveness with what she wrote after she married; whereas before
she married, the entire newspaper profession knew of her.
It was in the early years of her marriage that Mother began
to say, "We do have our Code, you know." And burned the
poems.

It seemed that marriage eclipsed a profession for a Luskin
woman. But perhaps it was more that, once married into The
Family, The Family became the profession, marriage the
business, and poetry something which a good, devoted wife
simply did not allow to interfere with her duties. Mother
played the piano so that she could accompany Da's return
from the office, dressing in her evening best, lighting the
candlelabra on the piano, and sitting down to begin to play
just as her husband would open the door. That was what she
did as a married woman. She did not ask him about work,
she merely played the piano melodiously, as if to assuage
him, and herself, perhaps.

She refused to discuss her newspaper career with anyone.
That had been another life for Mother, life with a maiden
name, life without the demands of the Luskin Code.

But to renounce utterly her career? To squeeze her life into
the bonds of the Luskin Code?

She got her own back, later. When Da became ill, he had

to depend on his wife's editorial judgment. Then, sitting by his bed, with her pad and pen, their marriage made phrases that were printed the following day. But it was part of the Code; after all, she could not refuse to help her sick husband; she had married him for better or worse. And the articles were assigned to him, Mr. P. H. Luskin. What went on in the sickroom before the pages went to press was no one's business but theirs.

The daughters remember the bedroom scenes as they sit, now, where their mother and father sat. They wonder if Mother considered her editing then as part of the Code, or whether it was her old self coming back, unable to resist the temptation of the world outside the house which she had given up when she married. Did she get her own back, later? Or did she fret, inside, at the sight of her husband lying in the sheets, losing his powers to think clearly?

They reach the books in the inventory which they all know to be extremely rare. Louisa puts her inventory down on the desk and says, "We have to do something about these. What do you think?"

"Well," Barbara leans back in the chair, "this is a little difficult." She waits for Sadie, who remains distracted, to pay attention. "It's my turn, now, I know, but the best thing to do with these, I think, is to negotiate between ourselves. We all know how valuable they are, and we have to find some way of distributing them. The problem, at least, my problem," Barbara says, taking a deep breath, "is that I have to make a bid for Tom. And I guess you both know which book he wants, and that you also know it's by far the most valuable book in the entire house. But what I want to get across is that I'm not thinking of the monetary value, I'm thinking of getting my husband the one thing that would really mean something to him."

"Barbara," Louisa says, "if it will make you feel less uneasy, I've been thinking about this for a while. I'd prefer a less valuable book, but one that would mean more to me personally. I don't know how Sadie feels, but—"

"Me?" Sadie smiles. "For a while I didn't know how we were going to work this out. But then I remembered that George said he wanted the Hoover book, and I'd like to get it for him."

> I paid $1,000 in 1919 for my set of the *Libre Belgique*. My brother's *Iconography of Manhattan Island* is listed in Weyhe's latest catalog (1954) at $375. Agricola's *De Re Metallica* is listed herein at the valuation given in our New York Appraisal Company's 1930 Inventory, namely, $200. P.H.L.

The daughters take the books without any disagreement, each daughter pleased with the way it works itself out; though Barbara feels a little uneasy to have the most rare book.

> 1 La Libre Belgique—1914–1918—
> Certified complete by Paul Jourdain—with autographed engraving of Cardinal Mercier—Full leather binding—*Barbara (for Tom)*
> The Iconography of Manhattan Island—1498–1909—New York, 1928—*Louisa*
> 1 Agricola De Re Metallica—Hoover—1912, Autographed—*Sadie (for George)*

The first editions present the daughters with the same problem, but diplomacy again allows them to divide them equally to each daughter's satisfaction and relief.

> 2 The Prince of Abyssinia—Johnson, 1759—First Edition—*Louisa (for Patrick)*

5 Works of Lady Mary Wortley Montagu—
Richard Phillips—1803—First Edition—*Barbara*
1 Don Quixote de la Mancha—Cervantes—with
autographed engravings by Gustave Doré—Gift
of P.H.L.'s mother to her husband for fifteenth
anniversary—*Sadie*

The books are a forgotten territory of ancient knowledge
to which the daughters now pay an overdue tribute. How
could they ever think of Da as weak? Even foolish? The
books alter their image of Da just as, gradually moving into
the more familiar realm of books which marked the daughters' educations, the books control images of their past.

6 Dante's Divine Comedy—translated by Longfellow—
drawings by Flaxman, 1906—*Sadie*
10 Boswell's Life of Johnson—Murray, 1835—Leather—
Barbara
8 Shakespeare's Works—George Routledge—*Louisa*

Louisa laughs. "You know," she says, tapping her new box
of cigarettes against the surface of her father's walnut desk
(which she hopes to get for her eldest son). "When I was in
college I failed my Shakespeare exam. I'll never forget it."
"You did?" Barbara takes a faint pleasure in Louisa's ad-
mission. "I thought you majored in English?"
"No, I majored in psychology." Louisa crosses her arms.
"I was the one who majored in English," Sadie says pertly.
"College," Barbara says. "Doesn't that seem like a lifetime
ago?" For all of the daughters, what was missing from their
educations was compensated for at home. College was only
a supplement to the Code which seemed to take care of
everything, socially and intellectually. For a Luskin daughter
to be at college was almost unnecessary—except that the high

standards of the Code required attending college, particularly since Mother had never received a college degree. She urged education on her daughters even before they could speak. Intelligence was insufficient without the proper training.

When Barbara was in college, a history major, she was being trained to be a young lady. Whatever ambitions she may have had in those days were supplanted by the reiteration, A young lady is to be a good wife. To desire a career was not to understand their mother. Like both of her sisters, her own children's experience at college had influenced Barbara, giving her later in her life a vicarious fulfillment which she had missed when she was in the Massachusetts hills waiting for a man. When she first began, about five years ago, to be involved in the local politics of her Michigan lakeside district, she had listened to many wives complain of their inability to pursue careers when they were supposed to be pursuing them, in their early twenties. But Barbara had found that she was grateful for her training, glad that she had been taught what gloves to wear for what occasions, what clothes were suitable for what party at what hour of the day.

When Barbara's children, Tommy, Jr., and Liza, were packed off to colleges, Barbara was for the first time struck by the difference between her generation and theirs. Certainly life had changed—one no longer even wears gloves— but one should never forget the past. The Code had sustained Barbara through a great deal, always there at the back of her mind, selecting, informing her how to act, what not to do. She could not abandon it. She waits, now, to see, as her children grow—too quickly—into adults, how the Code will manifest itself in them. It occurs to her that perhaps it will be unrecognizable; certainly it will be transformed.

She hopes that she has not failed to give them a sense of

what the Code is, how one uses the Code. Every Luskin woman had used it in one way. Barbara's aunt had been the first Luskin to invest in a strange and highly improbable idea of a Mr. Land for a camera that developed pictures all by itself. Mother had been one of the founders, with Henry Seidel Canby and Amy Loveman, of the *Saturday Review of Literature.* But Mother never put her name on the masthead. Barbara always respected Mother for her self-sacrificing devotion to Da. Mother had to live by the Code in her own way. Whatever children will and always do say, however much life seems to change from one generation to the next, there is always the pressure to live with things as they are.

And yet, one loves one's children, and hopes, somewhere, that they will not forget the Luskin initial wedged between Barbara's two other names, the Christian and the married. But already, Barbara thinks, there are signs that they will abandon the Code. She fears that she has failed in her job as a mother, as a Luskin. Of course, one passed on those stories, those Luskin legends diminished over the years into a few set sentences—into their own code. One has to set an example without imposing the Code. Let them see that the Code lives, and try to reach out one's hand with the Code to them, and not to hold up a wall, distancing—to reach, if one can, and still uphold the Code.

College, Louisa remembers, ashamed, was the one time she was free from the overwhelming constraints of the Code. She went to a small progressive college in Vermont against her parents' wishes. The college was built on the premise of unconventionality, of going against all the standards of success; there were no grades, and competition was frowned on. Louisa loved it; but she was never a diligent student. She created scandal. Her close association with the head of the psychology department produced a ring of buzzing rumors that Louisa never denied. And she always forgot those things that marked a proper young lady—like the time she forgot her gloves when she took the train to New York. Or the time she and her roommate broke the rules and took the car to the boy's college for the weekend. Or the time they printed a satirical issue of the college magazine. Or the time they sabotaged the chemistry classroom. She never was caught—the college didn't believe in punishment.

Now, she feels that, except for her work in psychology, it was a waste of time. Embarrassed to remember what a child she was in college, she wishes that she had not given in so easily to the marriage conventions suddenly upon her. She had delayed her dream of being a psychotherapist for twenty-five years. It had taken her two sons to convince her to go back to school to get her Ph.D. Patrick, too, encouraged her; in her all-male family she felt conspicuously female, with all the word meant in her upbringing.

Was it that word that made her angrily give up a career to try to love and touch and hold her sons as her Mother never held her—when it was difficult to love that way, when inside she wanted to wait just as Mother waited for them to speak and show the signs of intelligence? For Louisa, the Code had been converted into an inflated symbol of betrayal . . . the word stops, and the forgotten melody echoes dimmed in her head, dimmed by the story of her mother's arrival in the city which she never left. The tune did not echo then, in the empty chapel, the same way that it now echoes in Louisa's head, wafting up as she remembers her satisfaction in betraying the Code with another version of the Code, ancestral, unknown; the satisfaction of reminding them all that *it was over*. But she did not mean that the Code was over; only that she was gone, and without Mother to hold the symbol in place, Louisa does not know what direction the Code goes, where it leads, if it leads one to understand the word female.

For Sadie, the Code was simply the best part about being a Luskin. It was special. Her marriage, after happy years at college looking just as happily for a husband, was a model of the Code. Having three daughters pleased her beyond words. But then, suddenly her cute little girls were young women, and it all happened so fast that Sadie, rushing about, taking them to school and to church, cooking dinner, trying to make everyone happy, had not noticed what was happening. By the time they were in high school they no longer needed her. She had to do something, it seemed that no one needed her.

And then, there was always the problem with the money. As a result of good investing with George's advice, Sadie's trust fund has at this point tripled. But they do not touch that money; they live on George's generous salary. Sadie wanted money she could call her own. So, without her daughters to take care of, Sadie applied for a job working with children in a hospital nearby. She did not think of her work with the children, which finally put her into an administrative position, as a career, but only as a substitute for her family.

About a year ago, having never touched her own earnings, Sadie was asked to attend a conference in Texas to discuss her work in the children's ward. She was asked to give a talk on her reorganization of child care in hospitals. Sadie used her own money to finance the trip, proudly, finding herself in an atmosphere of professionalism. She liked it. Programs in all aspects of hospital administration were being offered, and, after her return, she discussed with George the possibility of further training. He seemed indifferent, but supportive of her work outside the home, and Sadie is now in a position of directing infant care throughout the city hospitals. Sadie's instinctual talent with children was made into a method; her simple ideas of care part of a system.

Then, Maggie returned from Europe with a young man. But Maggie had no intention of marrying. There was a need to marry Maggie just as there was a need to organize Sadie's pastime into a career. What had happened? Sadie was confused; the confusion led to a furious argument with her daughter, till finally she persuaded them to get married. How did these things happen? Marriages, aging, children growing up and child care turning into a serious profession . . . And the terrible thing was that she did not like the man Maggie seemed to be so in love with.

Sadie, unable to cope with all the rapid changes, began to visit Mother often, trying to talk with her; but the talking was just as difficult as it had always been. Sadie did not know what it was that she wanted to ask Mother. When she had finally won Maggie over, Sadie suggested that Mother meet him, planning an enormous luncheon at the country club to which everyone was invited. Fearing that Mother would disapprove of Maggie's choice, Sadie had tried to hint to her daughter that he should at least get his hair trimmed, or buy a new shirt. She'd even buy him a new shirt. But Maggie, who dreaded the luncheon and hated the country club, absolutely refused to play any of her mother's games. They both showed up at the Club in jeans.

Sadie flitted from one relative to the other, carefully planing the seating according to the course of the luncheon. Sadie had it carefully calculated that by the time dessert and coffee were served, she would be on Mother's left, Mark on Mother's right.

Sadie will never forget the moment Mother leaned over

to her and said, "We do have our Code, you know." Sadie felt that at that moment, in that aside, Mother had settled everything. She no longer cared about the blue jeans. Mark is good for Maggie. I love my daughter. Mother approved. They did have their Code.

But the Code is not simple, special; not a symbol; is not even just the way things are. It is something that gets dreamed through with each daughter of each generation, changing hands, now conducting the grab on its journey through space. A line of Luskin women, standing at the end of the line, and facing the end of the line: that too is the Code.

"We're getting old," Louisa says. Sadie giggles nervously. "Well," Louisa teases, "Sadie might be an exception." Sadie shakes her head, half-serious. "But these books," Louisa turns to Barbara, "they really take me back. I bet that our own children haven't even heard of some of them, except for a few of the stories around them. But the books themselves, they wouldn't mean anything."

"Oh, something, surely."

"I don't think so, in spite of their education. It's too far back, too old."

"You know," Barbara says, "I kind of like it. Being old."

"You like it?" Sadie's hands fly up to her face forgetfully.

"Sure. It has some advantages."

"Advantages? It's just depressing. I mean, Da was old." Sadie's face loses its smile for an instant, then it returns. "It's bad enough having to dye my hair—" The daughters all laugh. "I just keep thinking of Maggie just getting married and all that she has to look forward to."

"I thought you didn't like Mark," Louisa says, raising her cigarette up to her mouth and squinting.

"Mark?" Sadie covers her mouth. Then, suddenly. "Oh, Mark!"

"Yes, I thought you didn't like him," Louisa persists as Barbara looks on, disapproving of Louisa's intrusion.

"Oh," Sadie says, "well, of course I didn't like him before they were married. But now that he's my son-in-law I can't tell you what a pleasant young man he is."

"Now that they're married. What difference does that make?"

"What difference?" Sadie's religious streak tightens her shoulders stiffly. "All the difference in the world."

"Why, Sadie," Louisa says, finding the conversation interesting. "People don't get married now until they've tried it out."

"Living in sin," Sadie says, suddenly. Louisa finds it hard to repress laughter.

"You know what Patrick and I call it? Playing house."

Barbara laughs, quite openly. "That's great," Barbara says, joining in. "I like it. I really don't understand the way young people get married and fall in love now—I mean, they don't seem to do either."

"Maggie and Mark are in love." Sadie's mouth begins to feel dry.

"And married," Louisa says, "which seems to be more important to you than to them."

"You know," Barbara quickly says, to avoid an argument, "I found out for the first time just recently that Tommy Junior was living with a girl. It shocked me, to tell you the truth."

"Of course it shocked you," Sadie says. "He should have asked your permission."

"He's old enough to take care of himself," Barbara says, "and I don't think that permission is exactly what I wanted.

I think it was just the feeling that he was grown up. Liza, too. Though I think she would tell us, I really do."

"Well," Louisa says, "both William and Michael have lived with girls. It did take us a while to work out our feelings about it. I don't think that I completely approve of it. I don't mean morally, but I think it's a lot to deal with at that age. And might be too much. I mean, breaking up with a girl after you've . . ." Louisa doesn't finish. The lesson of generations is reversed.

"Well," Sadie takes the opportunity to speak, "I think they should ask permission, no matter how old they are. It goes against all my morals. Why," Sadie lights up, "it's a violation of the Code, which—"

"Which you always bring up," Louisa says. "The Code, the Code. It changes, Sadie. You know that."

"I agree with Louisa," Barbara says. "We can't impose the Code on our children if they don't want to hear it."

"Well, even if they don't—and I think that all my daughters, even Maggie, do, whatever you may think—the Code is still important. It applies to us."

"But Sadie," Louisa says, "we're not getting married. We're already married." Sadie is silenced suddenly. What was she thinking? "And marriage is just a different thing now. Completely different. God," Louisa says with energy, "none of us could ever have even thought of having the kind of careers then that women can have now. It's just like that exam I failed," Louisa continues. "I failed it because I had gone off for the weekend with my boyfriend. Which was quite shocking in those days, but I was always doing things like that. And failing that exam is like a symbol—"

"It's hardly symbolic," Barbara says. "It's just part of things."

"Oh," Louisa says, deflated. Her hope for an intellectual

discussion, which would have been interesting, fades. "What
was the name of the play?" She puts her hand to her forehead as Sadie begins to feel her throat completely drying.
"You know," Louisa says, annoyed that her memory's not as
good at fifty-one as it was at twenty-five. "The one about
those daughters, you know—that's it. *King Lear.* You know
why I failed?" Louisa laughs weakly. "It was because of the
stupidest thing. Not only did I waste the weekend before by
not studying, I'll never forget it, because it was so stupid. I
forgot completely about that other daughter of his, you
know, the sickeningly sweet one—what was her name?"

"Cordelia," Sadie prompts, is prompted.

"Yes," Louisa turns, "Was that her name? She was just as
awful as the other two."

"But," Sadie says from her place on her father's bed, "Cordelia came back to her father. Because she knew."

"Knew what?"

"How mean her sisters were."

They are underestimating me again. A voice makes it approach: their father's voice in their father's room. But the
voice is not Lear, no tyrant. *Love is not prescribed in the
Code. Or is . . . ?* Even in his room, his books, lined up like
Lear's faithful hundred, are divided by his daughters without resistance. In the cage of a fantasy, a mind incubated
from the world of moral upheaval, all daughters would be
Cordelias, who knew but did not speak, Cordelias singing
with their eyes stories of who's in, who's out. The Luskin
fantasy of a Lear—who of all the women had ever realized it?
None. Where are his eyes? Waking, 'tis not so. The voice
approaches, but remains out of reach; there is no tyranny
of lines, here. There are no secrets in this house; all the
books are read, will be read.

The daughters remember the evenings when Mother

would sit in the reading chair, and Da, sitting up, his chest draining, would listen. Every night this ritual repeated itself, never interrupted, the words he loved heard from her lips.

Barbara stands up, stretching her arms above her head; then turning at the waist, she spirals around to face her sisters. Her voice, at this moment strangely beautiful, husky, ripe, says, "Can you imagine what our lives would have been like without the Code?" The light begins faintly to bleed, renting the sheath of windowglass with pink stripes. "Sometimes, I feel caught in the middle."

"Caught?" Sadie says, her voice catching in the pink drift. She wants to lie down on her father's bed—flat as a windless lake of snow—and forget that her daughter is married. She leans against the bedpost.

"Yes, caught." Who's in who's out? "We grew up with the Code. And I don't think any of us could put what it is into words, but in our own ways, we've lived by it. We're caught because we'd like to hand it down to our children, but we can't. This is the end of it as we know it." She looks at Louisa, hoping that Louisa will not disagree.

"But we should put it into words," Sadie says, stubbornly. "Isn't that the whole point of everything that happened last night and even what's happened today? Yes, yes, one has to try. But it won't come out right. It can't. Because—I don't know why. It's like the room." Sadie tosses her blond head, struggling. "It's all these books. It's the Luskin Records. They're printed, they're fixed, they have something solid about them and they don't change, which is like the Code, except—"

"It's more than that," Louisa says quietly. "There's us."

"But the Code is us. It's who we are," Sadie says brightly as the air floats around her words.

"No," Louisa says. Barbara's hands make fists. "There's knowing who and what you are just as you. There's more to knowing yourself than who you are as a Luskin. There's more to it than being dictated to." Suddenly, Louisa remembers that there is one thing that none of them knows, and which is fighting now with their words. Inevitably, it would be she who had taken the diary and would now be in the position she always is placed in of knowing.

"Dictated to?" Sadie thinks she has heard the phrase before, though she does not know where. "But it's not a dictation. It isn't, not the Code. Barbara's right, it changes, Barbara's right—"

"It's not a question of right or wrong," Louisa tries to anticipate her defense.

"It's just accepting the way things are and always have been."

"Almost," Louisa adds. "It is almost the way things are. And the way things are not."

A marriage before and after it was made into phrases

"Now," Barbara says, hoping to put an end finally to this rambling. "Since we've been talking so much about it, what are we going to do with the Luskin Records? I'm sure we all want them."

"I don't," Louisa says flatly, turning away to light a cigarette. For the first time it crosses her mind that neither of her sisters smokes.

"Why not?" Sadie asks.

"Just don't, that's all."

"Well, Sadie," Barbara says, "since Louisa doesn't want them, I think it's only right, since I have the *Libre Belgique,* that you should have them. All right?"

"Are you sure," Sadie says to Barbara, but looking at Louisa, "that you don't mind?"

"No, not at all. In fact, I think it's nice that you should

have them. Now," Barbara pauses, waiting for Louisa to protest. But she does not. She sits quietly smoking, wondering how she will be able to get some time alone to read the diary, and wondering even if she should try.

"I guess we've finished with the important books then," Barbara says. "The attached sheet," Barbara turns to the back of the inventory, "says that the miscellaneous books are packed in boxes on the third floor to be given to the Georgetown library. That seems like a good idea." She looks at Louisa, who remains distracted, tapping the ash of her cigarette.

"We have to do the furniture, don't we?"

"Yes," Barbara says. "Why don't we begin with the curio cabinet?" She rises and opens the double doors with glass windows of a standing cupboard. The cabinet contains, according to the inventory,

1 Ivory Fisherman
Buddhist Prayer Wheel
3 Egyptian Figures—2500 to 3000 years old
Carved Japanese and Chinese Ivories
2 Bronze Buddhas
29 Japanese Netsukes (From Stove to Boat of Souls—
    See legends attached to base)

The grab resumes the shape of fingers moving, as the tape is again brought down by hands in small strips upon the curios, gradually enlarging to the furniture, staining it blue, red and yellow. The triangle breaks into movement, forward, grabbing

A mirror, a feather . . . Does she breathe?

A ROUND
OF STILLS

THE MESS OF IMAGES, STREWN AMONG THE MOTHERS' LAPS, photographs in varying degrees of likeness scattered around them, sitting in a circle, Sadie on the floor, Louisa leaning against the wall, and Barbara on the small window bench in a tiny alcove between their parents' bedrooms, taking out the stacks of pictures from the house of a box stashed away among the linens and miscellaneous pillows a few years ago (when the family gatherings grew infrequent), must be sorted, Barbara thinks, chronologically. But Sadie and Louisa are talking, oohing and aahing over each photograph, while Barbara picks up one after another silently, intently sorting them by generations: Luskins from the turn of the century in one group, Mother and Da and their daughters in another, and the families of the daughters in a third group. The Luskins have not passed through the generations unnoticed by the camera's eye. As if the Luskin Records and the Code combined did not yield enough, in each generation there has

227

been at least one woman intrigued with the actual image, as
Barbara, now, who sits engrossed, and Sadie and Louisa, who
shuttle them back and forth, absorbed in the stories attached
to them, are. From their grandmother, fumbling on the great
lawn of the Virginia estate with a crude box and blackout
robe; to their Aunt Sarah, Sadie's namesake, investing in the
surprisingly sound idea of Mr. Land; to Barbara, whose own
house is stocked with photographs from her trips around the
world; to Sadie's oldest daughter, who is a professional photographer, a record supplementing the diaries and letters has
been made. Mother, as a journalist, took photographs on as-
signment; but when it came to The Family, she insisted, at
Thanksgiving and Easter, that someone, usually an outsider, take pictures.

"Oh, look!" Sadie says, leaning over to Louisa. Louisa puts
on her glasses. "It's grandmother Luskin—see the double
chin?—and look at the baby on her lap. It must be one of us,
but I can't tell who."

"It looks like you," Louisa says, squinting. The woman
and the baby both stare into the camera surrounded entirely
by lace, the sleeves of Grandmother Luskin enveloping the
petticoats of the baby in a great web of white. "Except—"
Louisa squints again, "I don't think it is you. Look—" she
passes the photograph back to Sadie. "See the eyes?"

Sadie examines it closely. "You're right. It must be you!
But, Looza, what a fat baby you were!"

"That's just the petticoats," Louisa says uncomfortably.
Sadie carelessly tosses the photograph into one of Barbara's
groups, and then continues, as Barbara methodically picks
up an oversize rectangular photograph with serrated edges
and a brown tint. The photograph, of Da's family when he
was about seven years old, reminds her of a portrait she saw
every summer when she was a little girl. Forgetting her in-

tention to remain quiet, she hands the photograph to Louisa saying, "Look at this one. It's exactly the same as Aunt Mathilda's painting, you know, the one over her fireplace up at the lake?"

"You're right," Louisa says, looking up. "The painting must be based on this, but I don't ever remember seeing the photograph before."

"What a tall family," Sadie says, wondering how she could have reached only five feet five when her sisters were over five feet seven, and Mother as tall, if not taller, than Da. "And look at Uncle Adrian! I never remembered him as being so handsome." Barbara laughs.

"You know," she smiles warmly, "I always thought he looked like Abe Lincoln. And I remember once, I asked Mother why he looked like Lincoln, when I was about ten, I guess. And she said, 'He has the same aspirations.'" The daughters all smile, just as the adults around the little girl smiled at Mother's remark then, which Barbara did not understand. Adrian Luskin was the "genius" of The Family; and certainly the Luskins had to have a genius to maintain their style. His story, which has been repeated and exaggerated with every repetition, of his careers and his fortunes, his scandals and his discoveries, has become a legend which no Luskin questions, and every Luskin envies.

Adrian received degrees in law, medicine and geology. With his law degree he managed the "family business," under his mother's watchful eye, as his two older brothers refused. By his second year in medical school, he discovered a drug that helped alleviate hay fever, and made a fortune on the patent. With his geology degree, he devised a system for mining during the First World War which ingeniously made him a profit and robbed the United States Government of labor and returns. But the stories which the daughters,

told later when they were old enough, remember best, are
Adrian's romances. No doubt, Barbara thinks, grossly exaggerated. She cannot imagine that Abe Lincoln would have a
Communist, red-haired Polish woman as a lover. Nor a Mexi-
can nightclub singer whose songs wafted across the square in
Greenwich Village to Adrian's house where he sat smoking
his pipe next to his demure, beautiful wife, twenty years his
junior. No one in the entire family, except his adoring wife
Carey, ever forgave Adrian for converting to the "Buddhist
faith" (they would exclaim) and leaving his millions to a
small Buddhist community in Greenwich Village to found
a school. Adrian left the family nothing, except the memory
of his gaunt six-foot-six-inch frame and his Abe Lincoln
profile.

Among the women sitting now with the photograph between them, Louisa is the one who most adored her uncle.
She was the only daughter who was not afraid of him. She remembers what she has always kept secret, his one word to
her at her marriage: "Louisa, your husband is one of the
brightest young men I have ever met. You, I think, will come
out best." The memory pricks her.

"Here," she hands the photograph to Sadie. "Put it someplace."

Sadie, glancing at her namesake, and Maggie's namesake,
Margot Ann, sighs and then tosses the picture into one pile.
"We should have copies made of that one," she says, "it
really is remarkable." Though Adrian stands out among the
nine children, dwarfing their father, the family picture is a
model of family pictures, the Code caught inflexible in an
image: The Mother, sitting with the youngest on her lap,
smiling proudly as if to say, This is my brood; the father sitting near, his arm in hers, pensive; surrounded by their
children arranged by age in a line in back of them which

curls around to their smallest on the ground, the entire frieze bordered by drooping wisteria and a white ornate arbor, the bustles of the skirts and the shoulders of the suits crowded together in one large mass of a proper, well-dressed, handsome family, awesomely upper-class.

As Barbara continues to sort them out, she grows aware of the line of resemblance interrupted by an occasional discordance, the Luskins changing through the years. But one looks for the moment when the genetic promise was fulfilled, that moment in development when the indistinct features of the child suddenly coalesced into a Luskin face. Barbara, finding more photographs of her own family, the daughters as babies and Mother and Da middle-aged, begins to feel uncomfortable. It was a bad idea (she thinks) to begin this interminable task. We should have just had copies made of the ones we don't have at home. But the pictures exert the (by now) familiar pull on her, and her misgivings grow with her interest. Louisa and Sadie continue to talk randomly; now laughing over Adrian, now exclaiming over Da, now debating who is who. Louisa is pleased to be getting along with Sadie—it will make things easier later on. Sadie is overjoyed to be laughing with Looza, thinking it is best this way —and really is this way.

Barbara picks up another photograph, repressing her surprise at the way Mother looks; her hair not yet white, formed in waves around her head, her face, tilted slightly, as if to include in her gaze the family about her and the camera before her, with Sadie, fat and beaming, on her lap. Louisa sits, her hair in a blunt bob around her face, at Mother's feet. Barbara stands, teetering, between her mother and father, one hand on his shoulder, the other on hers, staking her claim to both. Da himself looks dark, already in shadow; he does not smile, he does not frown. But Barbara looks like no one around her in the picture, though she cannot pinpoint the difference. She begins now to look for more photographs of herself, wading through the endless pictures of everyone else, to try to see what happened, when she changed.

"Here." Sadie hands her one. "Do you remember?" Barbara looks at the photograph of the three of them, in their early teens, on horses. Again, the difference: Sadie and Louisa look like sisters, Barbara like a distantly related older cousin. But it is Louisa who looks different now. And, in the picture, it is Barbara, not Sadie, who is plump. Her horse is the largest; looking at herself, Barbara is ashamed at her ugliness. She was not a lovely child; Sadie was the lovely child. She tosses the photograph into its group, and continues to look for when it happened that she could be identified as Luskin.

"Oh, my God," Louisa says. "Look, it's the picnic. You remember, the big picnic in Virginia?" Sadie, taking the picture, tries to name everyone, dressed in their Sunday best, Mother in one of her famous "outfits," made out of bits and pieces of old things taken out at the shoulders, pinched in at the waist, anticipating the fashions of the forties; while all the other women are still dressed in the long straight sacks, with their pointed shoes popping out beneath. The great-aunts still carried their parasols; the "Sisters"—all the Luskins of Mother's generation called each other "Sister this" and "Sister that"—flaunting great brimmed hats. The photograph appears to be of randomly grouped people, unless one supplies the anecdotes: "See, Mother is standing with Mathilda, and look, Arthur is moving away. He never did quite approve of her."

"And there's Adrian," Louisa says, "alone with a drink. And look at his expression. He's regally disgusted."

"And there's me—I think that's me—running after Aunt Carey, that is Aunt Carey talking to Peter, isn't it?"

"And there's me," Barbara says, "with Da. And look, Aunt Sarah and Margot Ann are sitting off in the corner by themselves—"

"Probably," Louisa says, "making nasty comments about everyone." The daughters all laugh, relieved after these days of isolation to imagine themselves back into the Luskin skirts grazing the cropped summer lawn. Even Barbara welcomes the company of the photographs, thankfully not the actual people. (Actual people would have to include Oliver, who is conspicuously missing.) These photographs, on exhibit, graciously include only what Luskins considered proper; the Code, on view.

Louisa picks up a photograph. It was taken when the daughters were in their late teens, early twenties, not yet—but almost—married. They are dressed in identical white linen dresses, only the collars and the padded shoulders showing, each neck draped with a different length of pearls. The photograph includes only their faces, close-up, with their hair carefully waved around their shoulders in varying shades. But what makes Louisa hope that Barbara will not see the picture is that she remembers the photographer insisted that she, Louisa, was the eldest and should therefore be in the center foreground, with Barbara and Sadie placed slightly behind her shoulders on either side. Sadie's face is plump, her hair the fairest, and her eyes twinkling. Louisa looks dark, and her head, staring straight into the camera, though softer, her lips fuller than now, still reveals how thin she must be beneath the prominent collarbones on the edge of the picture. She is smiling, but her eyes are deepened by the broad brows above them. Barbara, standing in the back, looks very much like Sadie, but without the smile and the receding chin. She does not look like the eldest sister; Louisa dominates. Barbara's expression is fixed on the back of Louisa's head, and her pearls, hanging down the longest, pull her whole face down. Louisa remembers trying to tell the photographer that he was wrong; but he wouldn't listen. Barbara intervened to say that she didn't care—but the expression the photographer caught betrays her. Louisa tries to put the picture out of sight; but the deliberate motion attracts Barbara's attention.

"Which one is that?"

"Oh, just like all the others."

"May I see it?" Barbara takes the photograph, and instantly remembers. Hesitating at first, she then decides to say, "Do you remember, Louisa, how the—"

"Yes. I'm sorry."

"Sorry. What are you looking at?" Sadie asks. "Give it here." Sadie looks quickly at it, then giggles. "Oh, that was so funny, wasn't it? The way he thought it was Looza who was oldest, and—"

"Sadie," Louisa says, in Barbara's remonstrative tone. "I don't think that the memory is pleasant."

Sadie, undaunted, continues. "Oh, but it was so funny! And what's even funnier is the way that Looza does look the oldest, because you're so different looking."

"Let me see it again." Barbara takes it. There (she thinks) that's when it happened. Suddenly, it was Louisa who looked different, and I looked like Sadie. But there's something missing. Here I am looking like Sadie; there I am not looking like either of them, but you can't see it happening. She can't see everything, name everyone—when she should be able to recognize everyone, because she is looking at members of her family. But that is the point: Luskins diminished. Families stopped extending their arms. Just like the house in which everything that was ever a part of their lives as Luskins is contained, now splitting itself into three, the photographs contain everything before there was any division. And yet are divided into excluding frames, a still immovable mess. What used to be so easy—organizing, sorting, naming—is now encountered with difficulty, one image after the next, a definition to be resisted and surrendered to as one resists and surrenders to one's new name after marriage.

"Oh, look," Sadie says, anxious to dispel the heaviness settling on Barbara's lips (when it would be so nice to sit and tell stories). "Here are our weddings!"

The photographs, arranged in one large folder, do not mesh with their memories. The formal figures, smile-flash, stiff morning coats, starched silk, caught in the square of a photo, captures none of the rush, pulsing. Here is Barbara cutting the wedding cake, six-tiered, with Tom, both holding the ornate handle of the large silver cake cutter (tagged by Sadie), with champagne glasses and daisies all around them. Here is Louisa, mistakenly at the edge of the photograph, Patrick kissing her face, just visible, with groups gathered on the other edge, sipping. Here is Sadie, standing at the reception line, her veil falling to the ground around her, George standing stiff beside her, both holding out their hands to a line of backs, black-suited men and white-hatted women.

Here are three formal portraits of the brides: One looks just as a bride should look; the other, vacant and nervous; the other young and proud. Three individual poses.

Then, suddenly, the daughters come to the series of pictures taken just last year at Maggie's wedding. But simultaneously the daughters are struck by the marked difference between that wedding and theirs. The budding brides are dumpy, emaciated, wrinkled, stiff, flustered matrons, parading around Sadie's muddy lawn with their husbands—Tom, bold, too handsome; Patrick, guilty; George, bored. But, as they go through this set of photographs, which are in the majority bad, differences pop out: Maggie is not wearing white, but a bright print dress, the colors more flagrant in the bad color print. Pearls are looped crookedly around her neck. Mark, his wedding band caught in the sun, a mug of beer in his hand, is wearing a blue seersucker suit that Maggie made, wrinkled with the heat. He stands with his face buried in Maggie's neck, kissing her as she leans against him. Sadie is so ashamed by the photograph that she nearly grabs it away. They move on: Now they see Barbara and Tommy Junior, out of focus, in the doorway of Sadie's living room, Barbara pointing off to a group of Mark's friends caught in the distant corner of the picture. Now a picture of Sadie and Louisa that makes Louisa burst out laughing. Both sisters have their arms crossed in front of them, their weight on one leg, their hips almost bumping into each other, purple against lime green, as Sadie's mouth is wide open and Louisa's shut tight.

"Oh my God, Sadie. What could we have been talking about?"

"I don't remember."

"It must have been quite something, to catch us like that." The pictures of Maggie's wedding catch everyone at a bad moment, particularly embarrassing considering the occasion and the trouble Sadie went to to get a professional photographer (whose camera turned out to be broken). Luckily, many of the pictures were taken by a good friend of Maggie's, who took one photograph which could belong to any respectable wedding album: Maggie and Mark are seen in profile on Mother's terrace, just before they kissed. The dark ivy covers the back wall, providing a luscious background of green, just the background one would expect for a picture which sealed their vow.

But then, just after the kiss, he snapped Mother, tossing confetti, framed in a dirty silk hat, her face panicked. Barbara will not look at it. Louisa hands it to Sadie and lights a cigarette. Sadie stares at the photograph in her hand. *This is not Mother. Not her. It was my daughter's wedding when this was taken, when she looked like this, the round brim of her hat stained with age like the patches of her skin stained with the scars of operations.*

Sadie drops the photograph to pick up another. The other photograph was taken of Mother when she was thirty-four, only three years married. She stands beside a wooden bench, a closed book in her hands. Relieved, Sadie says, "What an angel. What a perfect angel Mother was."

(In their mother's bedroom, beyond their eyes, the sunset floods the brocades red, burning to amber.)

Barbara, remembering in her body, stands as she did last night when, challenged, she picked up her glass and then put it down. What she said, she remembers, was unlike anything she had ever said before. All day, through the grab, in the study out into the hall, from the trunk to her father's bedroom, through the books and into the tiny alcove, Barbara, though not thinking, has been looking for an answer to what happened last night. The answer should have been in the photographs, untouched by voices. But the answer is not in the photographs. Just like last night, the answer is

in Sadie's mouth—and Sadie should be strangled for uttering
it. But Barbara does not know if she wants to strangle or kiss
Sadie. Nevertheless, she should be bound and gagged, Barbara thinks, to stop her from saying lies. And I—I should
be handcuffed. Louisa, blinded. And now Barbara remembers what Louisa said and, giving up, leaves the alcove suddenly.

"Where are you going?"

"I—I'm going to phone Tom," Barbara says, on impulse.
"He should be at home."

"Well," Louisa says, putting out her cigarette and removing her reading glasses. "Help me stack these photographs,
Sadie."

"What are we going to do with them?" Sadie says, grunting
as she kneels to gather one pile into her arms.

"I don't really know. Why did we sort them out to begin
with?"

"It was Barbara's idea. I guess she has some idea of what
to do with them now."

"I guess,'" Louisa says, putting one stack on the seat where
Barbara was sitting, "it would be easy enough to copy some
of the ones we don't have. As for the rest—I don't care much
about them."

"Oh, I'm sure Barbara would like them. I couldn't possibly take them now."

"Now?"

"Not after getting the Luskin Records." Sadie pauses, putting her hand beside her mouth. "Why didn't you want the
Records?" she asks, quietly.

"Why? Oh, I don't know," Louisa hesitates, aware that this
would be a good time to confess. "I just felt that I had
enough things already—"

"That's just how I keep on feeling," Sadie says happily. "Exactly. So many and there's still so much more."

"Is there?" Louisa furrows her brows. "Sadie—" she begins.

"What?"

"Nothing."

Sadie folds her fingers in her lap, kneeling. Then, as she gets up slowly, she faces Louisa with her hands at either side. "I've been thinking."

"About what?"

"About the portrait." Louisa, who is also standing, crosses her arms in front of her, aware that she is at a disadvantage. "And I was thinking," Sadie says, as her own arms cross in front of her large breasts, "that she must have given it to Barbara." Louisa looks intently at Sadie, wondering what her sister is actually thinking. Louisa has assumed that Sadie would want the portrait more than any of them. Louisa doesn't want the portrait now; it is being replaced, as the grab continues, by other things.

"Why Barbara?"

"Because if she gave it to Barbara," Sadie says, carefully, hoping to express her well-worked-out thinking precisely, "then we couldn't fight about it. You see, giving it to Barbara is what a Luskin would and should do. Barbara is her namesake, and so giving it to her would be traditional and acceptable. And, I think, I really think that knowing Mother she would have thought that the best way to decide would be according to the Code."

Louisa is relieved to hear that Sadie, apparently, won't grab it away. But . . . "Sadie, I thought that you would want it most."

"Oh," Sadie smiles, "of course I want it. But that's not it. I've just been trying to work out in my mind how Mother

would think, not how I would. If it were for me to decide,"
she laughs weakly, "you know that I would take it without
a second thought."

"What's making you say all of this?"

"Everything," Sadie says, vaguely. "But mostly it was that
photograph of Mother holding the book. She was such an
angel," Sadie says, her hands floating now gracefully down
to her sides. "She wouldn't want to do anything to hurt us.
I know. I know her. I'm sure of it," Sadie insists, unsure.
"And it just occurred to me when we were talking about the
Code before, you know, in Da's room—it occurred to me then
that the only way to avoid hurting us would be if she decided
to give it to Barbara. Except," Sadie sighs, "all this doesn't
mean anything, because we don't know and the inventory
doesn't say anything and that's what is so painful. She didn't
tell us. I wish so much that she had told us before . . . Now
we would be so much easier with ourselves if she'd told us.
Don't you wish she had told us?"

"Yes, I do, Sadie."

"Do what?" Barbara says at the doorway.

"We were just talking," Sadie explains, "about the portrait, and I was saying that I wish she had told us before."

"Oh."

"Was Tom home?" Louisa asks.

"No. He didn't answer."

"What do you think?" Sadie asks.

"About the portrait?"

"Yes, because I was just saying to Looza that I think
Mother must have given it to you. The Code and everything."

"Me?" Barbara turns to go out of the room, her sisters following. Retracing their steps of the day, into Da's room
where they left the inventories, Barbara confirms her feelings

that Sadie should be gagged. "What makes you say things like that? There's no truth in it whatsoever."

"Oh, but there is, there's all the truth in the world! You see, if Mother gives it to you—"

"But she didn't give it to me."

"She might."

"But we don't know whether she did or not. So there's no point in discussing what we have no idea about."

"But I do have an idea about it. And it's a good one. It makes perfect sense. Please, don't you see? By giving it to you, we can't fight about it. But if she gives it to me or Looza, we will fight about it."

"You're not making any sense at all, as usual."

"You always say that just when you don't like what I'm saying. But I don't understand why you don't like it. Don't you want the portrait?"

Barbara, standing with the red folder of the inventory in one hand and passing her other through her hair, doesn't know where to move. Then, "But what's the use of wanting it? I mean," she says, noticing that Louisa's back is turned, "I don't think about it. I just think about where Mother could have indicated her bequest."

"But how could you not think about it?"

"Because there are other things to think about." Then, seeing Sadie purse her lips, Barbara quickly adds, "Sadie, listen. The more you think about the portrait the more you are going to want it. And by the time we find out, you will have convinced yourself that it's yours. So the best thing to do is to forget about it and wait till we find out, which will have to be by tomorrow night."

Louisa now quickly turns and says, "Let's stop. It must be about time for supper."

"Okay," Sadie says. Then, half-serious, touching Louisa

on the shoulder as they move out of the room, she says, "But I think you're just tempting me with food to stop talking."

As Louisa walks down the hall following Barbara, she says, "Sadie, you're absolutely correct. That's exactly what I'm doing." Two of the sisters laugh. The third wonders why her husband didn't answer.

The daughters pass the door of their mother's bedroom.

PHILOSOPHICAL
OBJECTS

LOUISA LIES DOWN ON THE BED. THE BEDSIDE LAMP IS ON,
warming lightly the maple cones of the bedpost. She fidgets
with the stems of her reading glasses, not yet ready to put
them on. Her eyes ache. Her throat tastes of cigarettes and
dinner. Sadie's a good cook—like Mother. I would really like
to take the nap I told them I was going to take. She left
Sadie and Barbara downstairs after a quiet and pleasant
dinner, during which Sadie entertained them with funny
stories about her dinner parties when she occasionally let the
roast burn, or forgot to buy the liquor. Louisa, listening,
envied her sister's obvious delight with her domestic adven-
tures; and watched Barbara listen with a wry smile. Louisa
sat, smoking, wondering about Barbara's life with Tom in a
different way—knowing that if Barbara had a mind to do it,
she could make good money as a politician, a leader, and
recognizing something in Barbara would never allow her to
earn more money than Tom. At the time, sitting there in

243

the fullness of dinner and lack of anxiety, Louisa respected Barbara's attitude, even though she did not agree with it.

But then, just after dinner, Louisa felt the pressure return and, offering an excuse, went upstairs. But at the stairs' landing she overheard Barbara saying to Sadie, who was busy looking for old newspapers and firewood for a fire in the living room, "Good. Then we can burn the letters while Louisa rests." Sadie whisks around; her blue eyes wilt. Louisa, watching them standing slightly disheveled amidst the yellow, red and blue markings in the living room, wants to rush to Sadie; but suddenly listlessness and failure enter her. She's never really known her sisters, and she feels as a fixed feeling that even when it is all over she will not know them. She goes upstairs conscious that Sadie and Barbara, though they probably would not admit it to themselves, will in some way feel glad that she has left.

I started off wanting to listen. Because I thought, We've never been through something like this before, and we never will again. Mother's death—it was the one thing that all of us shared. I expected some miracle, a dissolution of the differences we've cultivated and depended on for almost fifty years. The differences have only been more marked—in strips of yellow and red and blue—and yet, something is disappearing. Something closer to us than who we are.

Sadie still puzzles me—though, I guess, less than before. She's more intelligent, for one thing, than I ever gave her credit for. But her intelligence never comes through intelligently. Louisa smiles, not knowing why. Then, letting go of the glasses, she thinks, It's Barbara that baffles me. I don't know what makes her insist on things that will only give her pain. Like not mentioning the Frog Band, when it would have been so simple—but God, that seems like ages ago, not just yesterday. I can't put her together at all. Some of it's obvious, and I've known it for a long time. The oldest sister. Responsibility. Healthy, outgoing. Compensation. But it's her honesty that I can't understand. It's not that it's dishonest, though I would have said that a few years ago, defensively. It's just that I don't understand where it gets her emotionally. I don't see where any of us is going emotionally.

We take unexpected directions—like Barbara's direction last night. Postponing reading Mother's diary, Louisa lets what she has resisted all day enter into her mind. How did Barbara know? Did she know? There were three glasses on the table. Two of them underlayed with milk, the third empty.

No (Louisa thinks), it wasn't the glasses. It was the vases in the dining room, it was that I took out the flowers Mother cut fresh from her garden every morning. I remember waking up and wondering every day when I would be able to sneak down into the dining room and—the vases were on the dining room table, then—take out the flowers, careful not to let the water from their ends drip. That's right, I had to be careful because the water would stain the table. And I would hold my hand, cupped, after I let them drain into the mouths of the vases—and then quickly I would

What would I do with them? I know I didn't throw them away. Because Mother always put them back in. They were her flowers.

I won't have any florist perfuming my funeral. If you must have a service, do me the service

of taking away the flowers, putting them in the kitchen, waiting—for what? Mother never punished me.

—You know I always replace them.

At age ten Louisa abruptly stopped removing the flowers. Suddenly, at age fifteen, flowers were pinned to her. *Don't you think you smell sweet enough without that large clump on your chest? The poor boy sneezed . . . I hated*

And then instead of a bridal bouquet a pair of shoes

And then this morning the gardenia. Here. Inside.

Louisa sits up. Suddenly she remembers the odd reactions they all three had yesterday to Mother's note. Was it true—that a man wouldn't understand their experience? That a man wouldn't be interested in a grab? That if she told Patrick about the gardenia he would face the other direction? She does not like the thought. It feels facile to her, like putting on a silk print dress because you don't have time to take a bath. But underneath that facility, slipping out of her hands (carefully held under the dripping stems), is the feeling that somewhere close, inside her, she will never be able to understand, outside of the context of her mother's house, how she listens and how she speaks—even how she moves through the air—her gravity. She has feelings, lifted out of their mouths.

Throughout her marriage, Louisa felt that her words could be cut off at the stems by Patrick's swift arms. But she had to speak, and was trained to speak well, in correct phrases. But silence conveyed a network of emotions, of darker mouths in themselves complete, which speech itself betrayed. Active and passive voices.

With a jolt, unexpected, Louisa realizes, as if by cause and effect, that Mother wrote poetry only after she was married. So it followed, with the spurious logic of association, that the two were interdependent, the same with a difference. The difference is—I don't know. There is a difference, but where? Here. Me. Her. Now.

And then another series of thoughts comes over her, but

in a blond light; not a wash, but a mottled and moving brocade of gold—though the thoughts themselves are not beautiful or connected. It is the tension in the weave between the image of Patrick developed through their marriage and his separate self—the uncertainty as to whether they are made of the same material, correspond. Does she know him? Yes. No. What are her feelings? Inaccessible. Unutterable. In someone else's house.

What was behind those words? (What is my body?) A dangerous assumption that reality was underneath, internal, when everyone knows that there is another reality which day in and day out we live by. Reality of feeling. Day in. Reality of situation. Day out. Then where does the voice come from?

Her mind wanders back to Barbara. There, she thinks, is someone who depends on the day out (of here). Why? It always comes to this—why does she act as she does? I just can't accept it as fact. There it is again: There are no flowers in the vases. There is no light in the chapel window. There is the gardenia. Beautiful Dreamer. What happened? She burned the poems. They are burning the love letters now. By burning the love letters one emotional hurdle is removed—but another is placed in their mouths. She feels alone now with her marriage, its mixtures, the feeling that she wants to call Patrick but knows that she won't. Unsure, she remembers vaguely the events of the day, badly focused images of her sisters, their clothes, the bits of conversation, the sudden entrance of the Code, blocked, sharply focused, but then leading her back again into confusion. But Barbara is right: Our lives are inconceivable without it.

And her. Mother, repeating herself with every turn the daughters take. Mother always coming up. Mother there, because she isn't, out of reach, us reaching, and never meeting her, face to face, word to word. Immediately Louisa's energy returns. Putting on her glasses, she opens the drawer of the bedside table and, with the diary on her lap, opens it to the first page.

Downstairs Sadie sits across from Barbara, in the living room in front of the fire, the slowly diminishing pile of love letters between them. Sadie sits slouched to hide the wish which starts up, like an intake of breath, every time one of them tosses another letter into the fire without reading it. They have said nothing to each other. Barbara's watchfulness, slackening as the tedium of their movements numbs her, forgets that Sadie is not to be trusted.

"How was George when you talked to him?"

Sadie looks up, ready to break into a grateful smile, then checks herself. "George? Well, you know, Barb," Sadie sits back, "honestly, it was kind of strange. I feel like we've been here for two years, not two days. Don't you feel that way? I certainly do."

"I know," Barbara says. "The whole thing is just plain exhausting. And I want to get home."

"Ummmmm," Sadie says. "It's surprising, too."

"Yes, it is." Barbara stretches her fingers. "Sometimes I wonder—you know, just briefly—what Mother would think if she had any idea of what would happen when she planned the grab."

"She didn't plan it. You planned it. It was just, you know, the Luskin way of doing the whole thing."

"Odd, when you think of it. I never really approved of the tradition." Barbara laughs weakly at herself, watching a letter flare up, then crinkle to black. "I'm not quite sure I approve of it now. At least it's reassuring to know that this is the only time we'll have to be on this side of it."

"What a thought, Barb!" Then, quickly pushing the

thought out of sight, Sadie continues. "I guess we're all kind
of on edge about the portrait. But I guess it's more than
that," Sadie quickly diverts Barbara's appearing frown. "Because you see we all thought of Mother as so responsible.
And she was, really, a terribly responsible person, you know."
Barbara nods. "And I think it seems to us that she just wasn't
taking responsibility when she didn't tell us."

"You know, Sadie, that's exactly how I feel when you get
right down to it. It's not who she decided to give it to. It's
simply that she didn't decide."

"But it's more than that," Sadie continues as the pace of
their letter-burning slows down, to her relief. "It's more than
that because—because when George phoned me, you know?
I found that I just couldn't describe it. I mean what it was
all like. He kept on saying, What's happening? And I really
don't know. Isn't that funny? I really don't know. Nothing's
happening except that we're doing what is expected of us,
we're sisters in Mother's house, we're divvying up everything. That's what's happening, except that it isn't."

"Of course that's what we're doing." Then Barbara shifts
her tone of voice into the safety catch of sarcasm. "If Louisa
were here, she would no doubt have one of her complicated
psychological explanations for it." Barbara remembers dimly
her conversation with Louisa before the funeral, when Sadie
was out of the room. She pauses, looks down at the letters,
and thinks, This will take over two hours to finish.

"You don't like all that, do you?"

"No." Barbara throws another envelope into the fire. "I
don't trust it. It doesn't make any sense to me. All that sym-
bolism. I've never understood it."

"But what," Sadie says, noticing that the letter Barbara
just threw in isn't catching, "what if you're not sure? I
mean," she dips her head slightly, "what if you don't know

whether something really," the word squeaks out, "really happened or not?"

"But that's impossible," Barbara says flatly. She quickly resumes burning the letters.

"But Barb, that's what happened last night."

"Sadie."

"Okay." She winces. "Maybe I'm making too much out of it. Except I found myself thinking about Louisa's approach today, weird as it is. I never thought I would, you know, because I always thought like you (Sadie smiles) that psychology was just for people like Louisa—a little too tight and intelligent for her own good. And then the whole thing's so expensive, but I guess Patrick can afford it. Except I don't really know what I'm talking about."

Barbara looks up at her. "The whole experience is a little harrowing, and I guess it's taking more of a toll on all of us than we thought it would. But it's just a part of our lives, Sadie. It's just part of being in the Luskin fold. But I do kind of know what you mean." Barbara watches a letter slowly catch, then explode. "I've thought of things that I never thought of before. Like the Code, trying to define it. And, to be honest"—it occurs to Barbara that perhaps this is the first time she has been honest since she arrived—"I enjoyed talking about it with you."

"Is this part of the Code, too?" Sadie says. She thinks, mistakenly, that everything else is, but not burning the letters. "Barb."

"What?"

"How come we're doing this?"

"What do you mean?"

"I mean, how come we're not reading them?"

"You don't really expect me to answer that, do you?" Barbara feels instantly annoyed; robbed.

"Yes. I mean no. No, I mean yes," Sadie finishes, flustered but determined. "Yes, I do expect you to answer. Because if you don't then there is no answer. Because one minute I think, Of course, this is the only thing to do. And then the next minute I think, Wait. What could possibly be the harm in reading them? And we don't have to do this at all. Who says so?"

"To coin one of your phrases," Barbara replies, "Mother."

Sadie's lips purse, then, furious, she says, "You're not only doing that to make fun of me. I know you make fun of me. It's not that." Sadie's hand waves through the air. "It's that you're deliberately evading the issue. I'm serious. Why doesn't anybody ever take me seriously?"

"Because you don't."

"But I do. We don't have to do this. It would be so lovely, friendly, wouldn't it, just to read one?"

"I knew you were going to ask that when we started. I'm surprised you controlled yourself this long. There is no explanation. But if you would like one—a serious one—then the explanation is simply that I say it has to be done." Barbara angrily picks up a letter and, throwing it into the fire, on top of the accumulating ashes of the dead letters, she waits for it to be absorbed in yellow. It lies there a moment, wavering in the heat, before the flames take it in, grabbing it from all sides.

"You know," Sadie says, her voice less shrill. "Mother might have said exactly the same thing. You know, exactly. But with her voice it sounded different. It sounded completely different." Sadie leans back in her chair, smiling in apology and sadness. "That's what I miss the most. Her voice. That, more than anything else, makes me sad."

Abruptly, Barbara says, "I'm thirsty. How about some ginger ale?"

Smiling, Sadie gets up and goes to the kitchen. Barbara continues throwing the letters in one after another.

Louisa skips over the first few pages describing her birth— "difficult"—and moves into the rest of the diary. Some of the entries are only a sentence, describing the weather, what she cooked or had cooked, her plants, with usually a reference to her best lifelong friend, Frances. Her mother's handwriting changes from black and slanted script into a bolder more pronounced print, as if through the years she became more exact. Louisa is, initially, absorbed by the small details, entering into the mundane existence of her mother.

Spent the morning cutting and snipping and watering. Moved the plants to their summer places. As usual, first day of spring in Washington muggy. Overwatering a few. Frances says the coleus must be "nipped in the bud." News from the Club that the annual bridge tournament starts next week. Might not attend this year. Da too ill.

Met Mr. C and Mr. W for lunch at Michel's. Mrs. W with us. First time I met her: "Oh, Mrs. Luskin, I've heard so much about you from Max." "You will be relieved to hear that I have heard nothing of you." Such exchanges at the time embarrassing but necessary for both parties. Max particularly. Dislike the dragged-along-wife. Reminds me of the years covering the legislature in Albany and being forced to explain that, No, I'm not So and So's. I am a reporter from the Tribune. Mr. C (unmarried) mentioned a woman, Loveman, interested in contributing some poetry to the magazine. A start. It is good to be working again, even a little. Luncheon excellent, as always. Must get the cheesecake recipe. It is the meat, not the sauce, that makes his lamb so good.

Nurse's charts show that Barbara and Louisa had a fight

today. Two little black marks. "Mrs. Luskin, the little girls were taking a bath when Louisa maliciously soaped up Barbara till she burned." Punishment: No meals for a day. Louisa already accumulated many black marks. Stronger measures? Will mention it to Da, when his asthma attack is over. Always in the spring it comes on. Refill the prescription. But what can one expect of a four-year-old? Must be taught.

Deliberately Barbara made her slip and fall. Nurse didn't notice. And then, of course, Louisa took her childish revenge. No one asked the four-year-old what had happened, the assumption being not only that she was just a child and had to learn the difference between right and wrong, but that Barbara, even though she was only two years older, already knew the difference and so would never do anything wrong. But gradually, as Louisa reads more of the diary, she discovers that the apparently disconnected notes have their own kind of form. Every reference in the diary to the children—black marks, checks, punishments and rewards—is part of the inventory of things. Nowhere in the diary does Mother consider her daughters as people, only as part of the house, like the plants or the pillows, the scraps of material she will buy on sale.

She reaches an entry which records, in Mother's succinct style, a conversation with Da about how to raise children. None of them is named: only ideas, methods, procedures, systems; discipline, right and wrong. Turning the page, Louisa finds the sentence: *"Children are just rabbits before the age of seven."* She stops reading, and sits, stunned. Then she starts laughing and she cannot stop.

Sadie and Barbara sit, forgetting the letters, talking about their families. They speak the same language; they both feel comfortable, free to express themselves without Louisa's accusatory or unsettling insights.

"Yes. Wasn't it terrible? They grew up, just like that!"

"Oh, Sadie, it wasn't so terrible. When I think of it, though, I think that the most difficult phase was not when they were in their teens, but when we had to cut off their financial support. But of course one has to. They have to learn to earn their keep."

"Exactly," Sadie says, remembering her refusal to lend Maggie and Mark money after they were first married. "Yes, yes, it's such a relief that Maggie and Mark are now both at good jobs."

"Relieves you of the burden."

"Yes, and no. What's funny, Barb, is that since Maggie got married she's started to visit us more often. It's such a nice change. Whatever I think about him—I like him, though—it's such a nice thing to finally see that someone has been able to calm her down. At least, he can handle her."

"Oh," Barbara smiles, "I've always had an affection for Maggie."

"Yes, she's always liked you for being straight, as she puts it." This, Sadie realizes, is a direct compliment, which Barbara accepts. It seems to both of them now that they are finally speaking as they would like to, which is the way sisters can speak to each other, protected by the intimate but imposed label "sister," taped over an unknown person.

Upstairs Louisa slowly recovers. She glances through the diary awed at the minutiae, finding that now she is bored with it. In many ways, it is a very typical diary, except that there is no sense of the person keeping the record. Louisa gradually begins to feel that Mother is missing, even here. It is the constant unwillingness to take responsibility for her daughters. Not just Louisa, out of one scandal and into another. It is the lack of involvement, the absence of intercession. The lists, words, dates estrange Louisa and Mother, when they should provide a passage. For there is nothing in the entire book about how Mother felt. She records the experience of her nervous breakdown and six months in the clinic as: *"I learned how to pot and how to sculpt moderately well."* Louisa remembers Da telling them that Mother would be away for a while, not to worry. Louisa didn't find out until a few years ago that her mother had had a nervous breakdown, not what they called it then, but what it was. None of the carboned letters arrived during that time.

Louisa hated those letters, when they did arrive, regularly at the end of every week; knowing that exactly the same things were said to the three of them. News about the family: "Sister this did that; Sister that did this." Not once, how are you. But: Your teachers says that you are doing fine, Sadie and Barbara. Then a public scolding of Louisa. All carefully worked out. Typed. Clear. Impersonal.

Louisa now wonders about the woman missing from the diary, which does not even contain poetry fragments, though she was writing at the time. Who was she? The diary was like the lists that, as a game, Mother and Da would make up, which they compiled in a notebook Sadie took with the Records. Lists of What to Take on a Picnic for Twenty up at the Lake. What is Absolutely Necessary for an Automobile to Run, beginning with Engine, ending with Driver. The Morning, beginning, "Nurse bathes children," ending with "Water the plants." Who was the other woman? Louisa lies down on the bed, exhausted, about to cry, when suddenly she sits up.

Before Mother died, Louisa visited her in the hospital. Mother weighed eighty-three pounds; her eyes like crystallized blue quartz, her face and arms scarred with the lesions from operations. But her hair, though there was hardly any left, sprung out from her face and hung there like small clouds in a lull. Her body seemed to disappear into the sterile white sheets, as if she were entirely cloud—except her voice, that never rode in the air, but subdued it into obedience. Her eyes looking closely at Louisa were prepared to defy.

"Yes, Mummy dear?"

"I want to die," her voice said. Louisa sat wishing that she could smoke. "Would you please tell the doctors."

"What?"

"That I want to die." Mother paused; speaking tired her.

Then, she continued, "Will you tell them as courteously as you can that as far as I'm concerned my business is done. I'm quite ready to leave." She closed her eyes and seemed to doze. Then quickly opening them, she said, "And tell them I've changed my mind about the painkillers." During the later stages of the disease, Mother suddenly converted to Christian Science. She refused any medication, except the necessary cobalt treatments. She submitted to the operations; but she resisted as strongly as she could any drugs. She disliked the way they made her mind foggy. Despite that she had no faith in modern medicine after the first visit to the doctor, two years ago.

"I would like something," she had said, "to make me happy."

"What, Mrs. Luskin?"

"Surely you have some shot? I've been quite unlike myself since my husband died. Surely you have some shot that would perk me up?"

"Well, why don't we run some tests, and then see." Mother

nodded. The tests were run, and the doctor made another appointment to see her.

"Mrs. Luskin, I'm afraid that you have cancer."

"Oh, well," Mother replied briskly, "that's nothing new." The doctor, a new physician, asked for an explanation. "Well, forty years ago I had a hysterectomy because of a small malignancy." Mother apparently considered that sufficient, for she sat quite still and waited for the doctor to speak.

"And?"

Mother scowled. "And nothing until now, according to your tests."

"Well," the doctor said, shaking his head over this eighty-five-year-old woman, "we'll have to begin treatments, Mrs. Luskin. As you know, they are usually quite painful, but until we progress further in our research, it's the best we—"

"That's your business. It's mine to take the medicine."

Mother's idea of medicine was to read Montaigne's essays. She finally agreed, when she discovered that the cancer had spread into her lymph glands, to have a twenty-four-hour nurse. But she harangued her constantly. She didn't want to be bothered. There was still some business to attend to: a friend of hers whom she was trying to get admitted into The Club. Then there was the nuisance of that awful wedding, when Sadie should really have been more organized. During the day her right leg had swollen twice the size of the other. She had stuffed her swollen foot into her flat, yellowed shoes, with bows on the toes she had proudly made herself. In a strange moment of fancy, she came into the living room that morning saying, with a lift of her lips and brows, "Well, how do you like dancing shoes?" She flashed them at her sons-in-law. Then, as if to prove that she was fine, she commented on one of Sadie's daughter's dresses, saying, "Isn't that skin you're showing?" To which her granddaughter had replied, "Yes. It's intentional." "Just like my bows," Mother smiled, and, as gracefully as she could, she went into the dining room to prepare the bowls of confetti and the sherry.

But the wedding finished her. Since Da had died, her life had no life in it. The balance was gone. Familiar rituals, a lifetime devoted to taking care of him, reading his mail, the newspapers; playing bridge and canasta; giving him medicine—there was no longer anything for her to do. She changed nurses. She slept more often in the afternoons.

Louisa remembers Mother telling the story about the doctor in her singing voice, laughing and raising her eyebrows, assuring her daughters that really, they didn't have to visit her so often. She was fine. Then, suddenly, Mother telephoned all of them and informed them that this weekend they were to divide up the jewels. The four of them sat in Mother's bedroom, where she lay swathed in long white chiffons, looking like Isadora Duncan, the dancing drapes hanging behind her. Mother told stories, nodded, pursed her lips, scowled. Not to give advice. When it was over, she merely said, "Just as I expected. Barbara wanted the sapphire brooch; Louisa the Cartier necklace, though I've always thought it too extravagant even for a queen of Egypt; and Sadie the emeralds. Just as I expected." She then announced that the inventories were in their last stages of being compiled, in preparation for the grab. She brought out the will, which made the grab legal, and also gave instructions as to certain sums of money to be given to Jewel and other people connected over the years with the family; some money to relatives, or small gifts; and then the trust funds for the grandchildren. Mother said, "I was thinking, there's so little that is amusing now. Give the money to them now, as it would be interesting to see what they will do with it. And mind," she bowed her head, "that you don't tell them what to do with it. I'm giving it to them. As for your money," she said, "you got enough when Da died. Don't be impatient." She sent them back to their homes.

They weren't impatient; she was. Boredom set in, more deadly to Mother than the disease. And now, she had finally made the decision, looking at the walls of the hospital, to die.

It was her second stay in the hospital. The first time she had insisted on being put in with two other patients: she wouldn't have any special privileges. She amused them with stories; asked after their families; and kept the nurses running back and forth to bring the other two women things. She made sure that they were comfortable. "No, no. It's Mrs. Simon that wanted the water. And she also needs her pillows changed. And Mrs. Martin, did you or did they put you in that awful position? Nurse, she has an awfully sore back." It went on, day in and day out, with Mother giving orders, running the show. But this time in the hospital, Mother was too ill, and weak, to be with others.

Louisa got up from the chair beside Mother and went to phone her sisters, who were staying at 1331. They then went to speak to the doctor en masse. He listened to Barbara's persuasive arguments, but would not give in. "Look," he said, angrily, "I'm a doctor. I spend my life trying to keep people alive, not kill them. Your mother is a remarkable woman, but I can't possibly let her tell me how to give her treatment —particularly if that means no treatment at all. She's tough. She might pull through. I have to give her that chance." Louisa remembers sympathizing with his position; her own work in hospitals had acquainted her with this problem before. But, she thought, if he knew Mother better he'd do what she says.

They all went into Mother's room; but with one look she

told them to leave. "He's bringing you the morphine, Mummy dear." Sadie said.

"And?"

"And he says that he's going to continue treatment," Barbara said.

They all waited, expecting her to tell them to go. But instead she said, "Do you remember Dr. Tyler?"

"Yes," Louisa said.

"He was a good doctor." Then she closed her eyes and told them to leave. Dr. Tyler, the old family physician, prescribed medicine extremely rarely.

A few days later, Mother worsened. Louisa went to visit her, relieving Sadie. They were by this time all convinced that she would die, and so took turns with her. The doctor also thought that she had maybe twenty-four, perhaps forty-eight more hours. Louisa walked in.

"Please draw the curtains."

"There aren't any curtains."

"Please, the sun." Louisa lowered the hideous blinds. They rattled. Then she turned and looked at Mother in the dim gray light; she looked softer (from the morphine, no doubt); but her eyes were brittle and cracked into blue. Examining her daughter closely, Mother realized that Louisa had something to say to her. Louisa realized that, although she hadn't known it when she came that day, she was going to ask her mother the kind of question that one only asks when death removes one from taking the responsibility for the answer.

"You're going to ask me something, aren't you?"

"Yes. I was thinking of it."

"Well, out with it. Don't miss your chance." Her mother's face was rigid, prepared, the lines drawn in tightly, bound into the Code. When Louisa finally knew what she was going to ask, she waited, hoping that her mother would not break down and cry. Hoping that those defiant lines on her face would remain fixed. But Mother reached out her hand just before Louisa spoke.

"Mummy," Louisa said softly, like the small child she at that moment was. "If there was anything you would have done differently, what would it have been?"

Without a pause, Mother replied, "I would have loved all of you more when you were little. I would have loved you then." It snapped in both of them, instantly. But then, Mother sat up and her voice said, "But one didn't, in those days, raise children any other way. There were rules." Her face returned to its austere composure; her eyes firmed into solid discs. "I abided by those rules." Then, pausing, she slumped back on the pillow, and slowly smiled. "Odd, isn't it? I broke so many others."

"Yes, Mummy."

"Yes. Quite." Mother slept. Louisa sat, looking at her, wanting to curse and embrace her. She left.

But the doctors had underestimated Mother. For she lingered on, and showed signs of recovering slightly, against all the odds. "Confirms a theory of mine," the doctor said, wheeling her out as she waved to all the nurses cheerfully. "It's the ones who don't like it that live it out."

"Don't like what?" Mother asked.

"Treatment." Mother smiled approvingly. She sent her daughters back to their homes. Now Louisa thinks that she planned it to be able to die alone. She withdrew. She seemed to retract both her body and her statement. Within three days after her return to 1331 she died at night in her sleep.

Louisa's memory of their last exchange should pacify her. After all, hadn't Mother answered her question as she hoped she would? Hadn't she said what Louisa wanted to hear? Wasn't that enough? No. Because it was like all the other small exchanges in one's life which seem to let emotion spill out quickly; but then slip discreetly into forgetfulness in order, as Mother would say, that things should go on, and business be attended to: "We do have our Code, you know."

The Code, the situation for her entire childhood that things were to be done decently, and in order. Death lets . . . Don't forget to water the plants. Arrange the room. Morning: Make the beds. Evening: Tuck them in. Grab. Arrange the house.

In that one exchange between mother and daughter the house collapsed. Walls tumbled into tear debris. Floors lifted and broke. Words slipped out of the binding of the Code into another mouth, darker, a color impossible to predict. The color of feeling changing from golden to scarlet then deepening to purple till, finally, it crinkled to black. Mother died when she said how she felt. For in that moment, though she had prepared herself, fortified the muscles in her face, she had suddenly reached out with her hand, and, making the decision in favor of the one she loved, she had abandoned the Code for Louisa's sake.

Louisa now realizes that she is crying, her tears smudging the bold and swift words of the diary. Quickly, she closes it. She does not want to destroy its perfectly formed print. It was how Mother lived. As she closes it, wiping her face and streaking her makeup, thinking that she will have to wash, she remembers that she read the diary to find out about the portrait. But she found another face there, not the portrait. She had encountered the daily inventories, flowers, business, luncheons and recipes, family news, a few bits of dialogue jotted down. But she still does not know about the portrait. She doesn't care; she is exhausted, and, getting up, replaces the diary in the drawer. She goes to the bathroom to wash her face, not noticing herself in the mirror. Then, slowly, as she descends the stairs, Louisa reenters into the evening of the second day of the grab. Reaching the landing, she looks up at the portrait, but passes it quietly, without thinking, and slipping back into the kitchen she pours herself a Scotch, downs it, then, almost invisibly, enters the living room.

Sadie and Barbara suddenly stop laughing. "Looza! You frightened me. Did you have a nice sleep?"

Barbara turns in her chair, meeting Louisa's eyes. Immediately Barbara furrows her brows, ready to ask Louisa what she has really been doing. But Louisa, noticing the pile of love letters still on the floor, says, "I thought you were burning them."

"Oh," Sadie says, "we were. But we just forgot and started talking about all kinds of things, about the kids and the family and we just forgot."

"Well." Louisa pauses. She can imagine their conversation without too much effort. She thinks of the diary. Then, deliberately, she picks up the remaining letters and standing between Sadie and Barbara, blocking them from each other, she dumps the entire pile into the now-smoldering fire. The letters sit, white and cool, for a moment. Gradually the lower ones light, then suddenly they flicker golden and blue. Louisa watches, satisfied. The letters subside into black. Barbara rises.

"What?" Louisa turns.

"Thank you very much," Barbara says, her lips tight.

"You're welcome," Louisa says vacantly, without sarcasm. She steps back, as if the letters were still hot, and reaches for a cigarette. "Now," she says, tossing the match into the fire, "if it's not too late, we can finish the second floor. There's only Mother's room left."

"Do we have to?" Sadie says, staring at the tufts of ashes.

Louisa says nothing, waiting for Barbara. "Yes," Barbara says, "our business is done here. Thanks to Louisa."

As the daughters file out and up the stairs, they all think of two stone squares set in the dirt, side by side, under which are buried the ashes of their parents: to Barbara, engraved initials on rock; to Louisa, secretive caskets; to Sadie, the hard pillows of a frozen bed.

TRESPASSING

THE ROOM HAS BEEN PREPARED FOR HER DAUGHTERS BY DEATH and its code. As Barbara gropes on the wall for the switch to light the crystal chandelier, the three stand, tripleted, at the entrance. Then, flicking up the switch, Barbara leads them into the room; the feathers in front of the mirror on the dressing table stir like the delicate plumes of great aunts long since deceased. Roaming, the three wander silently to the various lamps in their mother's room. Sadie, with unusual calm, leans over to light the pair of lamps beside Mother's bed, glancing at the ceramic figures of lovers beneath the small shades, enveloped around the stem of the lamp as if it were a tree. The figures are removable; their embrace, set. On either side of the dressing table the antique candle sconces, early Victorian with electric bulbs replacing what were once candles, light when Barbara twists their switches. Louisa walks over to the pair of tall iron reading lamps, gaunt as her uncles Adrian and Peter, and reaching up she lights them. The mirrors around the daughters—Victorian and fragile reproductions of early Italian gilt—pick up the round eyes of the lights; but they do not reflect the faces of her daughters looking into each other's eyes. *Mirrors, feathers, she does*

Over three months ago an old woman sat breathing, shifting her weight in the antique satins of the chaise; she watched the lights change, anxious for action. Anxious for action, her daughers now place themselves among the lights. She was in the room and was the room—then. Then she departed. Now they arrive to find none of her coloring prayers, but only

1 Mahogany rebuilt Bed—Single Size. (Sadie sits on its edge, fingering absentmindedly the rough stitches rising into blooms on the bedcover.)

1 Chaise Longue and Pillow in Antique Yellow Satin. (Louisa sits in it, one leg over the throw of matching satin folded at its feet. Her hands are empty.)

1 Sheraton Mahogany Chair—Reproduction. (Barbara sits in it, her hair as combed as the wood is carved on the back of the chair.)

The one (1) Plain White Room-Size Wool Hooked Rug—Approximately 10′ by 15′—lies between the three of them like a blank letter.

Mother begins:

No doubt you have been waiting for me to tell you my story—though I warned you at the outset that all the stories had been told. Only the inventory remained, and that was purposefully left in your hands. But since the beginning you have altered the facts (switched the lights). I think I should restore the facts of my story before they are recorded inaccurately. The Code must not be violated.

You are correct when you say that you cannot imagine your

lives without the Code. But, unfortunately for you, you do not, even now, know what the Code is.

Unfortunately for myself, equally for all of you, I dislike stories about myself. If there are episodes of my life of which you are still ignorant, your ignorance has been precisely my intention. My resistance to stories of a personal nature is a resistance you have felt all your lives. Because of the general nature of the Luskin Family, this resistance has been passed on to my granddaughter.

Louisa places a strip of red on each of the reading lamps. Sadie claims the ceramic figures underneath the lamps with her waves of blue. Barbara puts a line of yellow across the back of each of a pair of Normandy Fruitwood Carved Rush Seat Side Chairs—Antique.

The inventories lie open on all our laps.

I was born in Madison, Connecticut, November 10, 1885. My father was a shipbuilder. The less said of him the better.

Sadie: The Thanksgiving I was ten grandfather stayed upstairs for a long hungry time. No one knew what he was doing. The grown-ups whispered about "the bottle." I wondered if they thought grandfather was a baby. Finally he came down the stairs and he did totter like a baby. The banisters bumped into him, and he was fat and red like babies are fat and red. His nose bulged. He sat down at the head of the table. Mummy poured me a whole glass of ginger ale. I picked up my glass when everybody was proposing toasts and I said, "Well, grand-daddy, here today, gone tomorrow," and I drank the whole glass of ginger ale in one gulp.

Louisa: It was my first date. As we went out of the front door, wrapped in our coats and scarves the winter I was fifteen, Grandfather yelled from the stairs, "Damn you and all of your offspring." In those days they never used the word "alcoholic." They merely told stories downstairs in the parlor, and the stories got louder as the banging upstairs got louder.

Barbara: He built ships out of mahogany. They were reproductions of old whaling ships, perfect models in each detail, which are still in the Madison museum. I remember, when we stopped there one Easter vacation, that I was surprised to find the ships were not in bottles. I expected them to be in bottles. But they weren't.

1 Terra Cotta Head—Grandmother Luskin—by B.K.L. *(Sadie)*
1 Bas Relief in Silver on Terra Cotta—"Bar Keeps Daughter"—Nude—by B.K.L. *(Louisa)*
1 Plaster Cast—"Woman of Champery"—Done in Switzerland—by B.K.L. *(Barbara)*

My own mother was a sprightly, ineffectual, empty-headed woman who decked her dresses in ribbons. My only sibling, Oliver, took after her. I know that she carried the financial burden—and we were what one would call nowadays "lower middle class"—but her burden never weighted her shoulders. She walked far enough off the ground that I resolved myself never to leave the ground. I was the outsider.

The Woman of Champery walks up an incline. She is gray, heavyset, with a square basket on her shoulders, and on her head a hat bowed at its ridge. From her right hand she extends a walking stick up the hill. The expression on the woman's face is as calm as the side of Mont Blanc seen from a great distance by an old man. The boots on her feet are molded from the rough clay of the hill on which she is walking. One can see no division between the earth and her feet, so faithfully did Mother forge them together with her tools.

1 Pair Small Vases—White Alabaster *(Sadie)*
1 English Antique Button Box of Buttons *(Louisa)*
1 Cloisonné and Jade Key Box *(Barbara)*

I wanted to be a pianist. It was my single ambition as a young girl. As I did not attend school with any regularity, and we could not afford a real piano, I asked my father to take a board and mark out keys for me. With sheets of music in front of me I practiced daily on the soundless board, music of wooden clacks. As my great-aunt had promised me her Steinway when she died, I waited impatiently for her death. I continued to practice, certain of receiving the Steinway. My great-aunt finally died. I expected the piano within the week. But on Sunday, when we went to church, the minister, at the end of his usual dose of religion, paid special thanks to the devout woman who had thought of the church at the hour of her death. Now there would be a piano to accompany our hymns. I resolved then in my prayers to earn enough money to leave Madison, Connecticut. I resolved never to play the piano again.

I thought it was the spirit
Years later, after her husband's death, the sound of "Für Elise" is heard on an old baby grand, bought at one of the last church auctions, bought back by Mother, returned to her toward the end by the forsaken church, "Für Elise" out of tune, the notes of the music clacking like wood from her long fingernails, as if the soundless wooden board and the piano she lost were being played simultaneously.

2 Wardrobes of Clothes
1 Beaver coat }
1 Mink stole } In Cold Storage

To my mother's horror, I hired myself out as a seamstress,

a profession for which I had a reasonable talent. I stowed my money away. Within a year I had saved enough for a train ticket to Washington, D.C. I don't know why I wanted to go to Washington. But I did. Every single stitch I sewed that year was sewed by hand; and not a single stitch was wasted on a piece of clothing for myself.

I went downstairs to the living room one night. Drawn across the windows were the brown velvet curtains my mother kept scrupulously clean. I pulled the middle one down, and, laying it out on the dining room table, with an undercover of felt to protect the wood, I cut myself a suit. I stayed up through the night and on into the next morning, sewing. I did not notice my mother when she came in; she floated out. I sat, silent, intent on my work.

Every stitch of that suit was made by my own hands. It fit perfectly. Without informing my parents, with whom I had nothing in common except a house, I left home a week later. I never returned to Madison, Connecticut. And I have never since owned a more handsome or well-made suit.

My parents visited us twice. That was two times too many.

Out of the closet Sadie takes a strange black chunk of material hanging on a hanger. She looks at it, then, scowling, holds it away from her body to display to her sisters.

"What is it?" Louisa says, putting out a cigarette. Walking over to Sadie she takes the peculiar object and unfolds it.

"Oh my goodness," Sadie says. "It's an old-fashioned bathing suit."

No it is not—that is to say, it did not originate as an "old-fashioned bathing suit" with, mind you, a hat to match. That strange black thing was originally a bridal dress. Not my own. You see, when I arrived in Washington (which was my city, I said as I looked down Constitution Avenue from Union Station), I discovered that a young woman is subject to the attentions of young men. I was, in short, courted. The courtships did not, however, prove to be serious until I had been employed at the *Tribune* and was earning my keep as a young cub reporter.

One night, when I was twenty-five, I was invited to a fancy dress ball. Knowing that I did not have enough money to afford a dress, I went to the church auction and found an old bridal gown which, with a few minor alterations, fit handsomely. Removing the conspicuous lace I was satisfied that the gown did not look like a wedding dress. I was pleased to arrive at the ball elegantly attired for less money than it cost me to get to and from the ball. As I was dancing with one young man, however, he said to me, "And how is the little bride tonight?"

"What little bride?"

I went home. I snipped and gathered and dyed the gown black.

There is not a single article in Mother's closet which has not been altered or dyed or made from scratch. Her mark is in every seam and tuck of each dress, suit, and gown. Her cotton blouses, too numerous to count, and her nylon night-gowns, too layered to find their shape, were once sheets and curtains. Only the brown velvet suit—what she wore when she arrived—is missing.

But when you tell the story of my arrival in Washington, you tell the story as a piece of romance, a Luskin legend. You persist in these distortions. You forget me. Why do you interfere? Why do you all insist on interfering? I should never have had that portrait painted.

> 1 Rhinestone Hand Mirror—Belonged to Grand-
> mother Luskin (Da's mother)—said She looked
> in it to see what she looked like the moment
> after he was born.

Louisa picks up the mirror and looks at her face to see what one of Mother's hats looks like on her head. The entire top shelf of Mother's closet is lined with berets, tams crocheted by hand, fur caps, wide-brimmed and felt with plumes, fur-trimmed tams, ribbon-trimmed furs, silk berets, an Italian silk straw, the old yellow silk hat she wore at Maggie's wedding, lying next to a black felt hat with a square top which Louisa is now trying to force on her own head.

"It doesn't fit." She hands it to Barbara.

"I don't want it."

"No," Sadie says. "I don't like black."

"But what are we going to do with all these clothes and hats?" Barbara asks, looking at the room which is strewn with Mother's clothes.

"Well," Sadie says, "I know that I certainly can't fit into any of Mother's suits."

"And I think I'm too thin," Louisa says, in front of the mirror trying on a large rabbit-fur hat. It fits.

"But I don't want any of them," Barbara says.

"But they are closest to your size."

"I do not want to wear Mother's clothes." Barbara begins to fold the blouses on the bed.

"Wait. It's silly to let them go to waste. Wouldn't some of your daughters like them, Sadie?"

"Oh, Looza. They'd never wear these things."

I would like to point out that the fashions of my day were not the aberrations of attire worn today. *Is that skin you're showing? Yes, grandmother, it's intentional.* And I, certainly, was not the one to place my body on view. Clothes used to be (she stresses the word) used to be what distinguished civilized human beings from uncivilized tribes. Furthermore, I had to wear suitable clothes to work. I wore a gray suit on the train to Albany to cover the state legislature. I wore a navy blue suit to the office. The extravagance of the purely social animal was distasteful to me.

Yes, I did work—what of it? I know, everyone nowadays, though you profess to be "liberated" (a peculiar term), makes a big "to-do" about being a working woman. There is nothing notable in applying oneself to a job. It is true that I founded the Women's National Press Club—though there were few members. And it is true that I was the only woman employed by a newspaper's editorial board. But I merely did my job efficiently. When I wired in a story from the capitol I wired in the story written: On one side of the page were my notes; on the other side of the page was the story. I used a stenographer's pad with a line down its center.

I am sure that you would like more information about my career. You may find all that you need to know in the issues of the *Tribune* from 1904–1918, approximately. If you care to read the few poems Max insisted on publishing against my will, you may look at the issues of the *Saturday Review of Literature* in the years following. As to all of this fuss and bother about being a woman—it is fuss and bother. One does one's duty.

And one does one's duty as a wife. I burned my poetry fully cognizant of my duty. One continues to do one's duty, and raises one's children according to

The daughters, having folded their mother's clothes, now stand around her room in front of the various mirrors trying on the hats, one by one.

If there is a story I have intended to tell you, it is, of course, the story of my marriage.

1 Pair Parrots (Wedding Present) Probably Meissen—Crossed Swords—Marks.

At the age of thirty-one I was still unmarried. Two men, with equal qualifications as husbands, were courting me. I enjoyed the company of each; I had much in common with each; I was equally pleased by each of them. This double courtship had been active for a number of months when, inevitably, I was proposed to—by each of them. Unable to decide, I resolved, as a practical measure, to duplicate two evenings.

The first evening I wore a lavender dress. It was spring in Washington. We left at promptly half past seven for a restaurant of which I was fond. We ate dinner together, and the talk was, as usual, pleasant. We then left for the theater. The play amused both of us.

To continue: We walked back through the streets of Washington which were, at that time, significantly different than they are today. On the way we passed an apple orchard which was in blossom.

"Oh," I said. "Aren't the apple blossoms lovely?"

"Yes," my escort replied. "They smell exquisite."

We walked past the orchard; soon arrived at my door. I told him that I had enjoyed myself thoroughly, but that I was still undecided. He kissed me on the cheek. I did not blush.

The second evening I wore a lavender dress. It was spring in Washington. We left at promptly half past seven for the same restaurant, where I ordered the same dish. We ate dinner together and the conversation was pleasant. Then we left for the theater, and I pretended I had not seen the play before. But the play was not exactly the same the second time, seen with a different man. We left the theater and began the walk home. On the way we passed by an apple orchard. On the fence surrounding the orchard was a sign which read,

NO TRESPASSING, marked with an x beneath the words. I remembered the sign from the previous evening.

"Oh," I said. "Aren't the apple blossoms lovely?"

There was a long pause as we stood by the fence, the NO TRESPASSING sign beside us. The man I was with said nothing, thus lessening his chances to be my husband. Then, suddenly, he leapt over the fence, broke off one of the branches of blossoms, and returning to the fence, he handed me the branch before he climbed back to the street side.

"Here." He broke off one of the blossoms and, without any indication of self-importance, he merely tucked it into my hair and we walked on in silence.

When we arrived at the door I said "yes" to his question posed more timidly this second time.

At our wedding Walter Lippmann is known to have remarked: "It is a marriage made in heaven." It was, of course, no such thing. It was a marriage made in a forbidden apple orchard.

The waves of blue tape beneath the ceramic lovers wrinkle at the edges. The bedposts, attentive, are marked with a strip of yellow, yellow which clashes with the satin. Sadie absent-mindedly fingers the rough stitches . . . Louisa's hands are empty. Barbara sits next to the pile of hats, lopsided, threatening to fall to the floor.

  1 Jade cup is tagged yellow.
  1 Small Sheraton Inlaid Box is tagged red.
  1 Antique Mahogany Box (On Top of Chest) is
     tagged blue.

Does no one want the parrots? I admit they are gaudy. Barbara, won't you take responsibility for them? They are engraved with initials I have never been able to decipher.

You could, I'm sure, trace them back to some branch of some family. And (Mother lifts her brows) perhaps the parrots might develop a healthy symbiotic relation with your frogs.

Barbara blushes; grips the arms of the chair.

Well. Louisa, surely you're interested? Your house might accommodate them better than either of your sisters' houses. I remember visiting your house a few years ago. The arches reminded me of Bach cantatas. The parrots might lessen the impact of those lofty doors.

No, Mother.

Well, Sadie, there you are. They really are more your taste than Barbara's or Louisa's. I'm sure that you would like them in your living room, wouldn't you? The parrots really go quite well with your decor, not to mention your personality. Well, Sadie?

No, no, Mother, no—I

The parrots are, suddenly, tagged blue

When the daughters all look up and into each other's faces.

Do they recognize?

By turning away they do lose—Don't they?

Four hours have passed since the daughters entered their mother's room. Four hours exactly. They all remember.

Three baby girls crawl along the floor. Their mother's skirt skims the floor just out of reach. Crawling faster they reach out, the fringe of the petticoat, sweet like candy, just out of reach, they are crawling after it, crying, their mother's skirt trailing along the floor, it is ahead of them, swish, they cannot grab it, the lace disappears beyond them to the other side.

And the child plops down on the floor to wail. The nurse gathers her up in her arms, offering no candy, offering no words of comfort, offering no escape from the house, gathering her up she whisks her up the stairs to bed where the child screams and kicks the white sheets kicks them off her legs

While the skirt whisks out of the kitchen and into the hall, trailing along the floor. Now it slips up the stairs, lapping against the steps—the lace skitters to administer his medicine. The children are locked in their room and must wait another four hours.

On her way to his room the fringe of her skirt halts outside their door.

"Nurse, can't you stop it?"

"Mrs. Luskin, if they are crying it is not because of anything we have done. The only way to teach them to stop crying is to show them that crying will get no results. Children must learn to discipline themselves."

"Let me in."

"No, Mrs. Luskin. Isn't that Mr. Luskin's medicine you are carrying?"

"Nurse, they are my children."

"Mrs. Luskin, I believe it is time for Mr. Luskin's medicine."

"They are my children."

"Do not interfere with my job, Mrs. Luskin. I know how to raise children."

The nurse takes the keys out of her pockets. She locks the door to the children's nursery. She turns away. Mrs. Luskin, standing at the door, watches the nurse's skirt disappear up the stairs, broken by the lines of the white banister.

She stands at the door, the tray of medicine in her hand. Inside her daughters are crying. She waits, her lips white, waits until the horrible, animal noise ceases. Then she turns abruptly, her lips pursed, her skirt wrapped around her ankles as she turns and disappears into Da's bedroom to administer his medicine.

I married a man who trespassed in order that I should never trespass myself.

We do have our Code, you know.

Her hats topple to the floor.

❧ THIRD FLOOR ❧

SLEEP

I WATCHED MY DAUGHTERS SLEEPING AND I DID NOT INTERFERE
with their dreams. For the record:

Sadie dreamt her hair was made of blue feathers.

Louisa dreamt she gave birth outside in a field of snow.
(It did, in fact, snow again last night.)

Barbara dreamt her arms were made of wet plaster so heavy
that she was unable to move.

Motion is pain.
The motion of generations is pain.

Of course, dreams are nonsense. They merely interrupt
one's sleep.

GOING

As my story is not my story, but the property accounted for, I will account for it.

Outside the sun has already begun to melt the snow on the iron furniture in the back garden into splotches like neglected bridal filigree, the remnants of a reception. It was late Sunday morning before my daughters assembled in the room in which Louisa slept, with their inventories open on their laps, to begin the last day of the grab.

"Are you sure," Barbara asked, "that you want to do this room first?"

"Yes," Louisa said, calmly.

"You almost sound like you want to leave," Sadie said. She sat on the old maple bed, exhausted. Her blue eyes were milked over with fatigue.

"To leave?" Louisa smiled. Odd; her smile. I don't recall her smiling in that way before—she looked like a stranger. "I do, as a matter of fact. Want to leave." She would.

283

"I don't understand why," Sadie said. "I was just beginning to get comfortable. I was just beginning to feel like I
knew you both." She forced her voice into bright tones.
"Aren't you a little bit sad," she said, "that this is the last day
together?"

"It's far from over, Sadie," Barbara said. "It has just begun. And it will take us all day to make certain that we've
covered the entire house."

"Funny," Sadie said, as if Barbara had said nothing.
"Usually I'd be in church right now. I'd be singing right at
this very moment. Well," she sighed. "I don't imagine that
any of my family has gone to church without me. They don't
all feel about church the way I do." A blessing, I think. "You
know, it sometimes makes me sad that I was the only one—
the only one of us who inherited Mother's feeling for the
church. Not that I feel exactly the way Mother felt about
God. But at least I have religious conviction."

Which conviction no doubt accounts for your hours of
choir practice.

"Wasn't Mother a Christian Scientist?" Louisa asked.

"Not exactly, no," Sadie said. "She didn't really believe in
all of that."

"What did she believe, then?" As if Louisa didn't know.

"Well," Sadie began to explain, with surprising accuracy,
"she believed—she believed, I guess, that there was—that
there was a way to do things and a way not to do things. And
I guess the way to do things, she felt, or believed that the
way to do things was prescribed by God. Which it is," Sadie
took a breath, "prescribed by God, that is, I mean, the way
to do things."

"Sadie," Barbara began, shifting her weight in her chair.
"Sadie, if there is a way to do things and a way not to do
things, regardless of God, this is certainly not the way to do
this thing."

"What?"

"It is very nice," my eldest continued, showing admirable patience, "that you would be singing in church right now. And it is very nice that you think you're the only one of us who—"

"Well, you wouldn't be in church right now, would you?"

"No, I wouldn't." Nor would I. "But just because I wouldn't be in church doesn't mean that I don't believe in God." Exactly.

"Well, do you?" Sadie sang out.

"I suppose I do—if God means knowing how to do things correctly." What I have been trying to say all my life: One does one's duty. I have always been proud of my eldest daughter's sense of responsibility.

"It sounds to me," Louisa interrupted, "as if you are talking about the Code, not about God."

"Yes, yes," Sadie burst out. "Yes, that's exactly what Mother meant by the Code. It was her religion."

"It was not her religion, Sadie. It was like a religion to her," Louisa said. "Her religion itself was something which she kept hidden and never spoke openly about."

"Yes," Sadie said, "yes, it was a very private thing with her."

"So private," Louisa continued, "so private, wouldn't you say, that it would be impossible to know exactly what her religion was?"

"So, why don't we drop it?" Barbara said. "And get down to the business at hand." An excellent procedure. Evidently I managed to keep my so-called religion from them without sacrificing the principles of that religion, principles which I feel satisfied I have communicated to them. One should never interfere with what has been ordained. Thus my daughters did get down to business and begin to divide Louisa's room.

Within a few hours the room had acquired the by-now familiar tags of red, yellow and blue. Louisa, of course, retrieved her maple bed; and Barbara seemed to have a particular interest in an old hunting print—*Accomplished Smashers*—which I have always considered hideous. The title alone, without the picture, would deter anyone from making such a selection. Sadie's turn came next. She rose from the bed to tag the bedside table, a nice piece of antique maple, fourteen inches by fourteen inches; when she noticed that the drawer was half open.

What's in here?" Sadie pulled the drawer out. Louisa sat up.

To everyone's surprise, Louisa said, "Mother's diary is in there." Which statement was, of course, absolutely true and directly to the point.

"Mother's what?" Barbara asked.

"Mother's diary." Louisa stared back at Barbara, waiting.

"What is it doing in here?" Sadie exclaimed, removing my diary from the drawer.

"I put it there," Louisa said.

"When?"

"Last night."

"When you were supposedly sleeping?"

"No, Barbara, excuse me," Louisa said. Louisa's voice fell evenly into the unsettled air. "I didn't put it there last night, I read it last night. I put it there some time the day before yesterday."

"And you didn't say anything?"

"No."

"Why not?"

"Because I didn't think I should say anything."

Sadie sat back on the bed and opened the diary. It is unfortunate that Louisa has an excessive confidence in her intelligence, for she is a careless reader. On the other hand, it is equally unfortunate that Sadie, and Barbara, who joined her on the bed, read better than she did. Louisa waited while her sisters read the first pages in silence. She smoked through one cigarette—a disgusting habit. Women in my day never smoked. That is, my friends never smoked. Others did indulge. When she finished her cigarette, she said, "I know what you're looking for. It's not in there."

"But of course it's in here," Sadie said.

"I assume," Barbara looked over to Louisa, "you have read through the entire diary?"

"No, in fact. I couldn't get through it. A lot of it is boring." Boredom depends on one's interest. Anyway, a personal record is of no consequence to another person. There is, however, the gratification of knowing that there is nothing in that diary which does not adhere to the Code, word for word. I am responsible for it. *A diary is for the others living.* And I am responsible for my daughters' passing on the Code to their daughters.

"This is simply and finally the most outrageous thing that has happened since we arrived. It beats Sadie." Sadie looks over to Barbara, her mouth open. "There is nothing," Barbara gets up, "nothing more outrageous than that you should steal the diary—steal it—and all of that stuff about Sadie and the inventory—that's nothing, that was peanuts compared to this. You—how can you sit there? Don't you have any sense at all of how you have violated the entire principle of the grab? Louisa, answer me. Answer me."

"Answer what?" Louisa looked up through the wavering smoke.

"Why did you deliberately steal Mother's diary without telling Sadie or me?"

"I didn't, first of all, deliberately take it. I found it in

Mother's room at some time Friday, I guess. But I didn't
find out about the portrait, so it doesn't make any difference
whether I took it or not or whether you take it or Sadie takes
it. Because it doesn't say anything about the portrait."

Sadie had sat on the bed reading throughout their conversation. She looked up at this point and said what I knew
she would say.

"Yes, she does say, Louisa."

"Where?"

"I guess you didn't see it." Sadie took out a small folded
note, on my Tiffany stationery used for personal correspondence. She handed the note to Louisa, but Barbara inter-
cepted it.

"Here. I'll read it." Barbara stood and unfolded the note.
Never let it be said that I did not take care of all my worldly
business. I did tie up all the loose ends.

"It says," Barbara began; but it was difficult for her to
read what must have come as a shock. "It says: My portrait,
painted when I was 44, is given to my second daughter,
Louisa Luskin Morell. Date: October 22, 1973. Signed, Barbara Knowles Luskin."

Louisa registered no surprise. She knew, and in fact had
known since before my death, that I had left the portrait to
her. She knew it when she visited me in the hospital. Louisa
would come in and she would lower the blinds. Sadie insisted that I see the sunset. Barbara insisted that I look out
the window to see the view. Because Louisa lowered the
blinds I gave the portrait to her. She is at fault for not informing her sisters earlier that I had made the decision in her
favor. And she knows the reasons. I need not elaborate further on the reasons here. They are no one's business but
Louisa's and mine.

"I know," Louisa said.

"So you did see the note," Barbara said, and sat down. "But you had to keep up the lie. I don't understand you, Louisa. This beats all. I suppose you thought you were sparing us the agony, when you knew that no one would be spared anything. This just beats all." Barbara's mouth retired at its corners.

"Barbara, listen."

"Oh, I'll listen. But what can you possibly have to say?"

"Will you both please listen to me?" Louisa turned to Sadie who now stood by the window, blank, the air hazy around her. "Sadie?"

"Yes, Louisa. We aren't saying anything."

"Okay," Louisa sat up. "I know that neither of you will believe me. I know that for a fact. But I did not see that note when I read Mother's diary last night. And I actually believed when I took the diary that I would find out more than just the portrait, who she'd finally decided to give it to. I don't really care about the portrait, which is probably what you both find most difficult to believe."

"Since it's a lie, I don't see how you can expect us to believe it," Barbara said.

"It is not a lie. Look, you're blaming me for something that Mother did. I didn't take the portrait. She gave it to me. The portrait itself in fact means very little to me."

"It's a lovely portrait of Mother," Sadie said. Frankly, I've always felt that it suffered from a lack of accuracy. But perhaps no one can adjust oneself to an image painted by someone else. There is that portrait, and quite a different portrait which cannot be given to anyone—unless, of course, one is willing to receive it.

"It isn't the portrait, Louisa, which you know perfectly well. It's that Mother gave it to you."

"It's the one thing that we didn't and couldn't grab," Sadie said. "Because Mother wouldn't let us grab that."

"I'll let you grab it," Louisa said. Barbara's forehead crinkled.

"What do you mean?"

"I mean, simply, that I don't want it. It's been given to me but I don't want it."

"You didn't explain," Barbara said to try to keep Sadie from interfering, "how you knew that the portrait was yours if, as you say, you didn't read the note."

"I don't think I can explain it." No reason why you should, Louisa. You might spare your sisters. "But I'll try." You would, wouldn't you? You would try to explain to them something that you cannot explain to yourself, and which was, furthermore, an entirely private exchange between you and me. You of all my daughters have the least sense of propriety.

"Well?"

"Well, when Mother was in the hospital, I went to visit her."

"We were all visiting her, Looza. Because we were taking shifts."

"Yes, yes, Sadie. In fact, I believe I had gone in to relieve you, Sadie, that afternoon when she looked the worst and we all thought she was going to die."

"Get to the point," Barbara interrupted.

"I'm trying, Barbara. If you would stop interrupting me I might be able to get to the point."

"Yes, Barbara," Sadie interrupted. "Let Louisa talk. She doesn't usually talk so much." Indeed, she used to be reliably quiet.

"Anyway, I went in and I knew, when I went in, that I was going to ask Mother something very important to me—and to her, but—"

"In other words, you asked her for the portrait."

"No, I didn't ask her for the portrait. You don't really think that I would do that?"

"I did," Sadie said quietly. Both her sisters turned to her. "I did, once. I asked Mummy if she wouldn't please give it to me. You see," Sadie continued, looking at the folds of chintz across the window, "we were talking about it one day, you know, just talking about it, because I used to come to see Mother here and we'd talk, you know, and Mother said that she thought the portrait looked less like her than it did like me. So I sort of said, just joking except I was serious, I guess, inside I was serious but outside I was joking when I said Wouldn't she give it to me since it looked so much like me? I said I had plenty of room for it, or something like that, I had plenty of room and I was so filled up with wanting it . . . ." Sadie paused.

"What did Mother say?"

"Oh. She asked for some tea, I think. She didn't say anything. But you see," Sadie turned from the window. "You see, I thought that maybe she didn't say anything because she had already decided. But then I realized that even if she had decided she was going to give it to me she wouldn't tell me, even if she did know, which is why I can't understand how she told you, Looza."

"She didn't tell me," Louisa said. "Not directly. We weren't talking about the portrait at all. I wasn't even thinking of it at the time."

"Of course you weren't. We were all thinking about whether she would die or not. Which is what she was worried about." No, Barbara, I wasn't worried about dying. That I was going to die, imminently, was a fact. From my point of view, I was already dead. With the exception of my portrait, my business was taken care of. *That is closed. It will stay closed.* It is with great reluctance that I inserted that note in my diary. But I could think of no alternative. I was, in the hospital, more concerned with the pain *The motion of generations is pain. I have accounted for all my sins but* A pain I was more than willing to endure. There is no circumventing death; and the pain of death is ordained. *I should never have had that portrait painted, I thought. But I could not unpaint it.* It is not a pleasant experience to die. Opening the curtains

"*There are no curtains.*"
"*Please. The sun.*"

was a greater pain than the cells digging into my belly. You had no right to interfere with my death by opening the curtains. You had no right *But there is and must be the invasion of the inherited house.*

"I went in and—I pulled down the blinds. The room was dark, and Mother lay there. I was convinced that she was going to die. But then—then she reached out and she took my hand." Barbara and Sadie listened, alerted by envy. "So, I asked her—I asked if, if there was anything she would have done differently." *Human beings are born to ask, Would you love me?* And now she repeats the sin. *The parent civilizes the offspring. When they learn to speak they learn error.* Louisa, stop.

"She said—you know, her voice rang out even then, at, what was it? Eighty-three pounds? And she said that she would have loved us all when we were little. That's what she said." Louisa's voice stopped, though it was too late. She had already trespassed where she was forbidden to enter.

"But then," Louisa said, "just after she said that she immediately sat up and said—said something about how one didn't raise children except according to certain rules, you know—"

"The Code," Barbara said. "Typical that she would not ever abandon the Code."

"No, Barbara," Louisa said softly, persisting in her sin. "You see, she did abandon the Code. She gave me the portrait. I mean, she gave something of herself. Don't you see?"

"But Mother was always giving of herself, Looza," Sadie said. "She was always giving. Why, she spent most of her life worrying about the welfare of others. Like Frances, she was always worrying about Frances. Or about Da. She spent her whole marriage worrying about him, taking care of him, because he was always so sick, and she had to be a nurse to him. Why, Mother was the least selfish person I know," Sadie said, her eyes beginning to penetrate through their milky haze. "She never thought about herself. She always thought about others. I can't think—I mean—I can't imagine Mother any other way. She was generous, kind. My God, Louisa, Mother was—"

"Yes, always thinking of others," Louisa said, losing the calm waves of her voice. "Always someone else. Never us, Sadie, never us, her daughters. And never herself—which is horrible. It's terrible not to care about yourself."

"I'm sure that's your philosophy," Barbara said. "You never consider anyone but yourself. And right now your selfishness is in full view. Giving us a lovely story about an intimate exchange between mother and daughter."

"But you asked me," Louisa said. "You demanded I tell you."

"All that I asked was for you to explain why you stole the diary. Which you have still not explained."

"Oh, stop behaving like you were God," Louisa said, disgusted. She did have a point. "I told you already, you can grab between the two of you for the portrait. I don't want it."

"You know perfectly well that we cannot grab for the portrait. The portrait is yours."

"Why can't we grab for the portrait?" Sadie asked. She, too, had a point; though a naive one.

"Because the portrait was to be given, it has been given, this note indicates that it has been given to Louisa, for whatever reasons, and therefore the business is closed." Barbara's arms seemed stuck to the arms of the chair.

Louisa paused, waiting for Barbara to calm down. Sadie sat still with the diary in her lap, afraid of speaking. Then, Louisa's voice returned to its even tone, and she said, "Barbara, why do you do this kind of thing?" It was a question of which I highly disapproved.

"What kind of thing?"

"Pretending that you're not hurt."

"Am I pretending that I'm not hurt? Thank you for your diagnosis. It just so happens that your diagnosis is wrong. If I am hurt it's no one's business but my own." Which comment expressed my sentiments exactly.

"But Barbara, if you are hurt it is because of something I have done. I would like a chance to apologize."

"For what?"

"For the fact that you are in pain." The fact that one is in pain is not a fact for which any other human being can be held accountable. It is a sin to try to go against what has been the inevitable fact of life since the beginning. We can only ask in prayer guidance to accept the will of God. *Kill me.*

"But not for stealing the diary?"

"Yes, sure, for taking the diary."

"I don't blame you, Looza," Sadie said. "I would have done the same thing."

"But you didn't," Barbara said.

"No, I didn't. But I would have, if I had seen it. I would have because I can't think of anything that is as close to Mother as her diary *Kill me* It is her own private record, you know, and I think all three of us would very much like to have it." Sadie is probably correct in her assumption. "But," Sadie said, looking at the leather notebook in her lap, "it doesn't really belong to any of us. Or it belongs to all three of us."

"Lovely," Barbara said, "would you like to divide it into three equal sections according to the pages?"

"Oh, Barb, don't be sarcastic."

"Well, what are we going to do with it?"

"We could draw for it," Louisa suggested. Rationally.

"But it's like the portrait, and we can't grab it."

"It wouldn't be fair whoever got it."

"This goddamned grab," Barbara said. "I wish it would just end. I wish there had just been one will and that was it."

I myself never considered the grab an efficient means of distributing the property. I felt, on the contrary, that because the property belonged to me I was held responsible for its distribution. But one never loses entirely one's sense of ownership, particularly if that ownership includes, as it does in this instance, the possession of all that was accumulated during my marriage to Phillip. It is to him that I felt the responsibility. I never felt the same after he died. *Kill me.* But, as the Twenty-third Psalm, his favorite, read at his funeral, says: "The Lord is my shepherd. I shall not want." *Whom you have already killed.*

"The basic problem with the grab is that we have to want things in order to get through it."

"But of course we want them," Sadie said, finally putting the diary on the bedside table. "They were Mother's."

"And Da's," Barbara said. "The difficulty, which has been

made clearer and clearer since we've been here, is that it never seems as if we are grabbing property. And it is impossible to avoid the difficulties inherent in the procedure itself. But all of this would have been avoided in a will."

"I don't think they are difficulties, Barbara," Louisa said, the cigarette now in hand. "The grab is a good way because we are allowed to take what we do want, what means something to us."

"Louisa," Barbara said, pulling the end of her ponytail, "you are remarkable." Louisa tapped her cigarette and waited. "You have certainly been allowed to take—to have what means something to all of us. Which is your superior vantage point."

"How many times," Louisa exploded, "do I have to tell you that I don't want that goddamned portrait of Mother?"

"And how many times do I have to tell you that it is yours?" Certainly a good number more than I had to.

Suddenly Sadie threw open the curtains which had been partially shut. She stood with her back to Louisa and Barbara as she spoke. I must confess that I have always considered Sadie a baby; but children have, at times, a remarkable ability, an aberration of nature or whoever created them, to say exactly what cannot be said, or perceived, by an adult. I would, of course, have listened to them when they were little, but for the fact that they had not yet learned to express themselves. Sadie, at that point, with her back to the window, expressed herself admirably, and quite to my surprise. I would never have given her credit; but one must give some credit to what is said by the naive and simple.

"If I were in church right now," Sadie began, her voice chilled by the cold window, "I would pray that God would show me some way to understand and accept that my mother had died." God would, indeed, help you with that fact. "And then, because I still can't accept it, I think I'd pray to understand why the portrait was given to Louisa." At this point Sadie turned, and her voice immediately warmed. "But I'm not in church right now, I'm here, and I think I have to understand it myself. But the only person who could explain it would be Mother, and she won't explain things to me. I remember telling Louisa yesterday that I thought she had given it to Barbara because that would have been sticking to the Code, and because if she had given it to Barbara then we wouldn't have been able to fight about it. I wish you two didn't fight so much," Sadie said. Louisa and Barbara did not look at each other. "But you do fight," she sighed. "And I realize now that no matter what had happened we would have fought about it. But what I'm trying to say is that maybe there's no reason why she gave the portrait to you, Looza—I don't mean to say that she didn't have a reason. Of course she had a reason because Mother never did anything without a reason. Never." Sadie now moved in toward her two sisters and placed herself on the edge of the bed between them. She obviously had something in mind. "But, since you don't want the portrait, Looza, which is also something I can't understand by myself—since you don't want it and it's yours, I don't see why we can't possibly find a way for either Barbara or me to have it, since we want it. And because I don't fight, I think we could work it out—don't you, Barb? Don't you think we could work it out?"

"No."

"But what's the point of Looza having it if she doesn't want it?"

"The point of Louisa having it is that it was given to her."

"Wait, Barbara." Louisa crossed her arms in front of her and paused, thinking. "There is something which I do want, much more than the portrait. I'd be willing to trade—I just can't remember which one of you two grabbed it."

"What? Grabbed what?" Sadie said quickly, her eyes now finally the familiar glazed blue.

"Well," Louisa smiled, laughing to herself, knowing that her sisters wouldn't be able to understand her—and I sympathize with her; the object she has in mind is without doubt strange. "You know those netsukes, the ones Da brought back from Japan?"

"That were in his bedroom? In the curio cabinet?" Sadie said.

"Yes. Well, there's one I would be willing to trade the portrait for."

"I can't believe it," Barbara said, beginning herself to smile at what appeared to be an absurdity.

"It happens to be true. There's one of those netsukes which is a boat, you know? The passengers on the boat are, according to the legend Mother typed, souls being transported to hell and to heaven. The great thing about it is that the boat looks as if it could be going in either direction, that is, to hell or to heaven, you can't tell. The waves that are carved into the sides of the boat could be going one way or the other; the man at the bow could be the man at the stern; the expressions on the faces of the souls look joyful and miserable. I'm sure you've seen it, because it's the largest and most detailed." Louisa looked at both Sadie and Barbara. "Well, that's what I want." The expression on Sadie's face conveyed without any uncertainty that the netsukes had all been grabbed by Barbara. The boat, especially, appealed to Barbara, but for other reasons than its appeal to Louisa. I myself was quite fond of those small Buddhist talismans. They are extremely valuable, a fact which I'm sure all my daughters have considered.

"Well, Louisa, I can't say no. But it certainly does feel odd to trade that one small netsuke for Mother's portrait."

"Never mind," Louisa said. "I happen to like that piece more than almost anything else in the entire house."

"Looza, you're crazy," Sadie said. "You're just crazy."

"I can't really say anything to deny it, Sadie. It must look crazy to you."

"It does," Sadie said, thinking of all the things she had grabbed which she was sure Louisa would want—the vases in the dining room . . . Oh, no, Sadie remembered. She'd already traded those off for the living room rug. Confused, Sadie simply sat not knowing what to say or what to do. I think she was beginning to feel just then a desire to leave.

Barbara noticed Sadie's distraction. "Look, let's not decide now, okay? Why don't we wait until we're through with everything before we deal with that. I'm not confident that I would like to trade; I feel as though I am going against Mother if I alter her decision."

Sadie lit up. "Yes, Barb. We shouldn't go against what Mother did decide. Absolutely."

"So," Barbara said, relieved, "let's finish these rooms."

My daughters then began to take turns, fulfilling the demand made upon them by the Luskin tradition which I refused to alter myself.

GOING

THE SUBTRACTIONS AND ADDITIONS OF THEIR LIVES ARE NOT THE
time I know. That is to say, I would not trespass on the feelings of my three daughters throughout the latter part of the
afternoon as they finished the rear guest room—Barbara's—
and the small guest room known as Cat's Sitting Room, in
which Sadie slept. A painting of a cat done by Sadie's eldest
when she was fifteen is, perhaps, the most notable object in
that room; notable for its lack of talent. Barbara, though I
do not know why, grabbed all my sculpture tools and the
empty casts of a few unrealized pieces. I cannot imagine what
use she could have for them. Sadie, predictably, chose the
cartoon for "Silver Swans." Louisa took the set of Curtiss
Blue ceramic jug and bowls I made during my second convalescence for my husband. By the time they had finished
these rooms, which composed nearly the entire third floor,
the sky matched the ceramic jug. The temperature dropped.
But, as I said, the subtractions and additions of their lives

are not familiar to me. I am only familiar with the subtractions and additions of my house.

Of all the houses in which we lived throughout our marriage of fifty-four years, 1331 was the smallest. I never
adjusted myself to its cramped size. Like any woman, I have
my own dream house. But of course the house one would
wish to live in is never, in fact, the house one finds oneself
living in. As it went, day in and day out, 1331 was satisfactory. In each room there was sufficient exposure to grow a
variety of plants; and plants generally thrive in the Washington humidity. Not Da—Da suffered; but the plants always
bloomed with regularity. The back garden, to which I was
particularly attached, offered magnolias, a few azaleas of mod-
est pink and, at one time, camelias. I have never attempted
to grow vegetables.

The houses repeated themselves, they filled and emptied.
But with each house the filling diminished and the emptying
grew. The first house was so large that one could ride a bi-
cycle on the third floor. But the last house was so small that
only a doll could ride a toy on the third floor. The house
in between, 1407, was a house filled and emptied in pairs.
1407 was a house not to forget.

The frame of a house determines its contents. The estate
in Virginia contained the Sheraton pieces; and in Virginia
we acquired three daughters. We moved to 1407, and there
we acquired the foreign pieces from Da's travels. The walls
in 1407 were covered periodically with tapestries and prints.
It was in 1407 that my portrait was painted. While living in
1407 we also received that portrait of Da from his mother.
The floors in 1407 were gradually patterned by rugs. The
mantels were populated by the Meissen courtiers and cherubs;
the Capodimonte box was filled with Da's butterscotches.

Finally, it was in 1407 that we acquired three sons-in-law, and subsequently lost three daughters. They left in pairs, and thus what we lost was multiplied by two.

When we moved to 1331 there was only Da and myself in the narrow halls and the narrow stairs. Da, of course, could not climb even the smallest flight. We had elevators installed immediately, those small two-seaters that rode up and down along the side of the staircase. I remember the grandchildren at Christmas riding up and down and up and down until the elevator broke and had to be repaired.

What had fit into 1407, fit into the skeleton of the house, was never accommodated to 1331. One could barely move in the living room; the china threatened to topple off the mantels; the rugs crimped in the corners; the wall panel of one thousand and one Buddhas covered the entire west wall; the Flemish verdure extended beyond its borders like a badly kept garden. But what was one to do? The frame determines the contents, but one only carries the contents to the next house; one takes what has filled the house, never the house itself.

And now 1331 has finished its division into three. The one house in which I died has split into three houses across the country: one in Connecticut, one in Maryland, and one in Michigan. By the end of this week the contents will all be packed into boxes by a moving company, loaded into trucks, and driven to the three houses of my daughters where the objects will find a new place, though the objects themselves remain the same from one generation to the next. Of the next generation, my daughters' children, I have no predictions. It takes years to build a nest; and nests are less predictable than one would think.

All that is left in my house to be divided is

MISCELLANEOUS
(Throughout Residence)
Linen—Bedspreads—Blankets
Shawls—Costumes—Silks—Laces
Briefcase—Bags—Suit Case—Trunks—Picnic Kits,
   etc.
Vacuum Cleaner—Carpet Sweepers—Brooms,
   Dust Pans, etc.

What one needs, in short, to clean the house and to leave for an assortment of occasions; and all that one needs for sleep upon return, except the bed. The bed is gone.

When my daughters arrived at the last page of the inventory, MISCELLANEOUS, they arbitrarily divided what was stuffed into closets and hidden in cabinets overlooked during the past three days. Sadie took the bedding; Louisa the materials; Barbara the trunks and cases. They left the vacuum cleaner and the other household articles. I suppose they thought that the house would benefit from a thorough cleaning before the new owners arrived.

The new owners will be strangers. At last I know that I have seen the end of my houses filling and emptying with parts of me.

Sadie: My living room will look identical to Mother's.

Louisa: The house I have always wanted is a house in which everything can be found.

Barbara: We won't keep a schedule. We won't take any trips, but we'll stay at home and look out the window at the lake.

Their passage down the stairs and into the kitchen unfor-

tunately took them past my portrait. They might have taken
the indirect route through the living room, but without
thinking they went the most direct way. None of my daughters stopped in front of the portrait. As Sadie began to cook
dinner in the kitchen, and Barbara and Louisa fixed themselves drinks, Sadie began to talk.

"Well, girls," she said, as if she were addressing her daughters and not her sisters. "It's just about over now." She smiled
as she turned to place the food on the table. "And it's been
so wonderful, don't you think? I just think about these three
days and I feel so relieved and happy that we've finally gotten through it. I feel so happy that we've finally gotten
through it and I feel so happy that we all, all have what
we want. You know," she continued as Louisa and Barbara
exchanged eyes then looked away, "I think that the most remarkable thing of all is that we managed, somehow, to get
what we wanted. And that's what I just can't get over," Sadie
laughed, sitting down. "What I can't get over is how nothing
I wanted interfered with what either of you two wanted. Oh,
yes, we do have our Code, we really do. Why, it's like magic.
And we're all so much closer to each other now. I knew, I
just knew, even before the grab began, that we'd get to know
each other better, and you know? We just never see each
other, and you live so far away, Barb," Sadie reached out to
touch Barbara on the shoulder. "And Mother brought us all
together and I feel warm and close to both of you.

"Oh." Sadie served the food. "Oh, I know that we've had
some differences. That was to be expected between Luskins.
And a few odd things happened, which could also be expected of Luskins. I was just thinking about those letters, you
know, and I wanted to read them so badly, and I do, I really
do think it's a shame that we didn't read them because it

would have been by far the loveliest experience, by far. Oh, Barbara, don't look at me like that! Of course I'm not blaming you, I'm not blaming you for anything. I wish you hadn't felt so strongly that we had to burn them, but you did, you did, and I understand that we had to burn them, but it's still a shame. But as it is," Sadie turned to Louisa, "as it is I feel that we've all got so much of Mother, each of us, we're each taking her with us." Sadie sighed. "I mean, I guess that what I am trying to say is that the most extraordinary thing about the grab is that I feel my faith has been confirmed in a life after death."

"In a what?" Louisa broke in.

"In a life after death, Looza. You know, I finally understood that Mother died. Her house is gone. But you see, the way that I understood how Mother had died and was really dead was by understanding that she was alive in us, and I know, I'm just certain that that is exactly how you two must feel because it is a truth, a truth about the way human beings are on this earth, an unchangeable truth. The very best thing is to know that there is a reality to confirm our faith. A reality that there is a life after death."

"Sadie," Barbara said, her voice impatiently tight. "You are confusing your own life with Mother's. But there's no point in discussing it now. We have to deal with the matter of the moving company's arrival, who is going to stay to supervise the packing. And we still have not settled the issue of the portrait. So, the grab is far from over. Louisa," Barbara said, "why are you smiling?"

Louisa was, in fact, smiling a broad and uncharacteristic smile, one which did not appear to fit her face. "I don't know," Louisa said. "I guess I'm smiling because I feel glad that it is almost over. I feel like laughing."

"What's funny?"

"Oh, nothing's funny. Nothing's funny at all."

"Well, if you feel like laughing be my guest."

"But I don't want to laugh by myself."

"Well, I'm not in the mood to laugh with you."

"Neither am I," Sadie said, sullen. But then she brightened. "Only, Barbara, there's one thing which we don't have to worry about because it's all taken care of."

Louisa looked intently at Sadie. Sadie, apparently, has still not learned to contain herself.

"The new owners will arrive next week," Sadie said cheerfully. I'm sure that the new owners lifted her spirits. Louisa then began to laugh to herself quietly.

"The new owners?" Barbara said.

"Yes. Looza," Sadie turned. "I don't think this is funny."

"It's not funny, Sadie." Louisa could not restrain herself, however, and her face lifted at all its corners rudely.

"Sadie," Barbara said, trying to ignore Louisa. "Are you trying to tell me that the house is already sold?"

"Yes. Isn't that nice?" Sadie wanted to giggle with Louisa, but Barbara's questions distracted her.

"When was the house sold?"

"Oh, some time last month," Sadie said. "But I don't know any of the details, Barb. You'll have to ask George about—"

"George?"

"Yes, of course. He takes care of all these matters."

"Of all what matters?"

"Why, the estate."

"Why," Barbara said, her mouth tugging at her teeth. "Why weren't Louisa and I consulted?"

"Consulted?"

"Yes."

"But, Barb, that's why George is the executor. So that you two won't have to be bothered with silly things like finding people to buy the house."

"Sadie, I am not paying your husband a thousand dollars a month so that I won't have to be bothered—"

"Paying him what?"

"His pay, from the estate."

"Oh yes," Sadie said. "That little bit really helps."

"How much did you say?"

"One thousand dollars a month."

"Is that how much I'm paying you too?"

"Oh, not me, Looza, not me. George. That's what George gets."

"Good God," Louisa said, beginning to laugh, "I had no idea it was that much."

"And he just loves doing it," Sadie said. "He really loves it."

That my second daughter pays no attention to her finances is, perhaps, a fault in her training. But her husband's considerable wealth allows her to neglect money matters. From the expression on Louisa's face, however, it would appear that she was having second thoughts about her negligence. I myself have very little to say on the subject of finances within the family. The finances were entirely Phillip's business, and he was the person responsible for George's being the executor of the estate. I will, however, make one comment: He might just as easily have designated Sadie, for it seems that she rather enjoys what is supposed to be George's job. Which fact struck Louisa as amusing, apparently.

"What is so funny?" Barbara asked.

"Oh, I don't know. I don't know. I guess just that I'm paying a thousand dollars to Sadie—"

"To George, Looza."

"Oh, Sadie, I don't care. It's just so funny."

"Well, I don't find it as amusing as you do," Barbara said. "Sadie, what did you sell the house for?"

"You mean George? I didn't sell the house. I just found them."

"Found who?"

"The new owners. And they're so sweet! They're a lovely young married couple. And they positively adore the house. They fell in love with it at first sight. You should have seen—"

"But we didn't. Sadie, what did you sell the house for?"

"Oh, I think it was something like fifty thousand dollars. Something like that. Give or take five thousand."

"Give or take? Which one?"

"Oh, Barb, I really can't remember. They were so sweet— that's what's important, isn't it? I mean, who lives here? Isn't that what's important? I mean, what it was sold for doesn't mean anything compared to who will be living here, and they were just so in love with the house and with each other, you know, married and everything, that I just couldn't—I mean, George just couldn't ask them for more than they could afford. I mean, we just couldn't, not after showing them through the house and—"

"That is dirt cheap," Barbara said, "for a house in the middle of Georgetown large enough for a family of at least four. That is dirt cheap, Sadie. George should know something about real estate."

"But, Barbara, they—"

"I don't give a goddamn about your couple. The point is that the money you don't care about—which is peculiar enough—is partly Louisa's and partly mine. Louisa may be in a financial position not to care, but I—"

"Oh, I care," Louisa said, "but in a way, Sadie has a point.

I mean, it does make a difference who lives here."

"See?" Sadie said to Barbara.

"Sadie, this is absolutely unforgivable. I am not paying George so that he—or you—or whoever—can find sweet people behind my back and not put a house on the market for what it is worth. What is so goddamned funny about this?" She addressed Louisa.

"It's just that—Oh, I don't know, Barbara, I don't know. I just can't believe that the house has been sold! Sold! To strangers! My God, if they had any idea what we've gone through to move out so that they can move in!"

"I don't think that's funny."

"Neither do I," Louisa said, smiling broadly. "I think it's pathetic." Louisa, my daughter who never laughs, then burst out laughing.

"I'm afraid that you're angry with me," Sadie said.

"Oh, Sadie," Louisa said through her laughter, "It's no use being angry with you. It's absolutely no use, is it, Barbara?"

"None whatsoever," Barbara said, now catching Louisa's laughter.

"It's funny that you two are laughing," Sadie said. "I mean, I'm the one who laughs."

Which statement caused Louisa and Barbara to double over with laughter, and then Sadie caught it. At this point I was so ashamed of my daughters that I find it difficult to describe the scene: the air bounced and their lips danced in the most unseemly manner. Someone should have told them to be quiet, but it was impossible to silence them.

"Oh, dear," Sadie said, wiping tears from her cheeks. "Oh, dear. We have to go home tomorrow," which made Louisa and Barbara throw their heads back.

"I'll tell my husband," Louisa said, mocking Sadie, "what a wonderful time we all had."

"And I'll tell my husband that I changed deeply from the experience," Barbara said in an even voice like Louisa's.

"And me," Sadie bubbled, "I'll tell George that we took care of business and that we had an awful time, and it was absolutely awful but it was interesting, oh so interesting," Sadie said. "Oh, oh, what are we going to do? Stop it, stop it."

"I can't."

"But we have to stop laughing. I have to stop laughing. My stomach hurts."

"No, no, don't stop," Louisa said.

"But I have to stop," Sadie said, trying hard to quiet herself. "I have to stop because I can't stand it, I can't stand it."

"Oh, God, this is silly," Barbara said, blushing deep red. "This is the silliest—"

"I have to stop now," Sadie said, her voice suddenly receded. "I have to stop. Please, both of you, we have to stop because—"

"Why?" Louisa said.

"Because we haven't—" Her sisters quieted down. "Because we haven't yet figured out what we're going to do."

"About the moving company? Well, I—"

"No," Sadie said. She pressed her fingers to her chest. "No, I mean the portrait."

Barbara's hand went to her face. She rubbed the laughed-out lines from the edges of her mouth. "Well," she said, reaching for her drink. She took a sip. "You're right. We haven't settled that issue."

"And we have to," Sadie said, "we have to settle it."

"I guess we do," Louisa said, lighting up a cigarette. Sadie looked from one sister to the other. None of my daughters knew what to do at that moment; they did not know in which direction they were going or they could go. The house was still.

"I have an idea," Sadie said, quietly. "It's very very difficult for me to express. Because I have to know first if you have both decided to trade the netsuke for the portrait. Have you?"

"We haven't talked about it," Barbara said, looking at Louisa. "I'm still uncertain."

"It's up to you," Louisa said. She stared impolitely at Barbara until Barbara was forced to speak.

"I want the portrait, of course. And it's a simple trade. Which is probably what makes the decision impossible: It's much too simple."

"If you think of me it's not so simple," Sadie said.

"Well," Louisa said, "I guess it isn't." Sadie sat still, waiting.

"Do you really want the netsuke?" Barbara said.

"Yes, I do," Louisa replied. "It means something to me. It's as simple as that."

"Doesn't Mother's portrait mean something to you?" Sadie asked.

"Yes, of course it does. But not as an object I want."

"You know," Barbara said. "You know what the problem is? The problem is that you're right. You almost make the portrait itself sound insignificant—wait a minute, Sadie. What I'm trying to say is that the portrait—well, I don't mean to go on. I think of how I was named after Mother, and her portrait reminds me of that. Although I do agree," she said, turning to face Sadie, "that the portrait looks the most like you, I am myself aware that Mother named me after herself. And that does mean something. At least, to me."

"So?"

"So," Barbara said, and stopped. She reached into the pocket of her skirt and took out the netsuke. "Is this the one you were talking about?" She handed it to Louisa, who had reached out for it as soon as it appeared. Louisa held the small carving in her palm, where it fit, perfectly.

"Yes," she said. "This is the one." She handed the boat of souls back to Barbara. Sadie watched the boat cross the table from one sister to the other, anxiously waiting to discover which direction it would finally go.

Barbara held it in her hand, shaking her head. "I don't understand. This?" Sadie pressed her fingers to her lips, wondering, hoping that the boat would finally cross back to Louisa.

"Yes," Louisa said. She was not smiling now. She, too, was waiting to discover where the boat would go.

Louisa kept her hands beside her. Barbara held it close to her face and then, without a word, she handed it across the table to Louisa, who reached out and put this small carving on the table in front of her. She let the boat rest. Still, the boat looked as if it were moving. The carving was so expertly done that it required no extra hand to make the boat move, or appear to move, backward and forward. I imagine that the Buddhist monk who possessed it had himself endless amusement pondering the direction of the craft carrying the souls.

Again there was a silence before Sadie spoke. "Well," she said. "Well. I guess that means that the portrait now belongs to Barbara?"

"I guess so," Barbara said, but she did not sound pleased. She sounded, on the contrary, skeptical.

"Barbara," Sadie said.

"Yes, Sadie?"

Sadie took a breath and plunged. "Barbara, I've been thinking, you know? I've been thinking and I thought that I really don't—I mean, I really do want the portrait and I was thinking that it is so simple to trade, it really is so simple and such a good way of doing things, you know, I was wondering—I mean, I. It's very difficult, Barbara, it's very difficult, but I was wondering, you know, because I want the portrait more than anything I can think of, more than even

the dining room chairs, and even though you didn't then—
didn't want it then, you know, I was wondering if maybe you
hadn't changed your mind? Of course, it's very difficult to
give up—but I just can't—I just can't imagine leaving the
house without the portrait—it just doesn't—settle—you know?
sit right in my head without the portrait—So, I was thinking,
and much as I love it, and you know that it brings back such
fond memories—well, it's just about the one thing I would
trade the portrait for."

Louisa interrupted. "She's offering you the Frog Band,"
she said.

"That's right, Looza," Sadie smiled. "How did you know?"

"I figured you would come up with something."

"Is that what you're offering me?" Barbara said, in disbelief. What she found hard to believe, Sadie's persistence in
trying to obtain what was not given to her, or the pain this
decision presented to my eldest caused her, I don't know.

"Of course, Barb."

Louisa sat looking at the boat of souls. The boat drifted
from one side to the other side of the table in her imagination as she looked at the tiny craft of passengers: an old
woman, a young Oriental girl, a man with a cloak, a woman
wrapped in cloth, a market woman, a small baby, an old man
and a young man, and the man at the stern and the man at
the prow who looked like two sides of the same man.

"Excuse me," Barbara said. She left the room quickly.
Sadie's hand, which reached out to stop her, reached out
too late.

My eldest daughter, my namesake, walked into the living
room and over to the southern window bay. She stood there
between the two tiers of the Frog Band on each side of the
bay. A frivolous child's object, in my opinion.

But I admit that I, too, enjoyed my husband's highly

original, if peculiar, talent for imitating the gurgling song of the frogs. An awful sound, but one that delighted my eldest daughter. She finally learned to speak the strange music almost as well as my husband, who, apparently, learned it from the frogs themselves.

My namesake stood there rigid. She might have been having a conversation, as she used to during the picnics up at the lake, with the small frog orchestra. The frogs that lived in the lake did not nearly match this full orchestra of clothed frogs. Yes, it is a ridiculous piece of furniture, a cute ornament in itself. But as she stood there, the summer game with her father must have been in her mind.

My husband's illness was difficult for Barbara. She wrote to him regularly from Michigan. Her letters arrived every Tuesday. Toward the end of my husband's life, her letters marked out the time for him. I might, and did, tell him the day of the week; but the day did not register unless it was Tuesday, the day a letter from Barbara arrived. He nodded acknowledgment that another week had passed and he was still living. It was his own foolishness that he entrusted himself to doctors. Why he let them perform that experiment— but enough. Privacy is the special privilege of the sick.

Suddenly Barbara left the place where she was standing and went out to the hall to confront my portrait. She said nothing out loud. She merely looked. It is impossible to look at the portrait for any length of time without seeing Sadie gradually appear over the features of a face that was intended to portray mine. But if one blinks, takes a step back, and looks again, fresh, as Barbara did, I appear clearly. The difference between Sadie and my portrait is Sadie's smile, a difference that even a stranger could easily discern.

When my first child was born there was no doubt in either Phillip's or my own mind that our eldest should be named

after one of us. I am pleased that Barbara refers to herself as
Barbara Luskin Fine.

Barbara returned to the kitchen and sat down. Louisa and
Sadie, expecting a decision, looked at her. Sadie's fingers
depressed her lips into a frown. Barbara said, "What are we
going to do about the moving company?"

"Barbara!"

"Just wait a minute, Sadie. I want to know what we're
going to do about the moving company and just exactly how
we are going to pack all of these things to make sure that
none are stolen."

"What did you decide?"

"Sadie, will you just sit tight?"

"I can't."

"Well, you have no choice."

Louisa turned the boat the other direction to see if looking
at the other side made any difference. As she did so, she said,
"I think that maybe you should stay, Barbara. You're the
only one of us who could probably make sure that everything
was gone and nothing overlooked." Barbara looked at Louisa,
a small smile appearing on her face to thank her. Louisa
dropped her eyes to the boat: The boat still seemed to move
backward and forward.

"Okay, Louisa. Sadie, do you have any objections?"

"It's so much easier for me to do it," she said. "So—"

"I was thinking," Barbara interrupted, "that I'd phone
Tom and ask him to fly out here to join me."

"Oh," Louisa looked up and smiled. "That's a good idea.
A really good idea."

"But I'm closest," Sadie said.

"I thought you had to work tomorrow," Barbara said.

"Work? Work? Oh, my, yes. But I only work in the mornings. I'm free in the afternoons."

"I think you've done enough, Sadie," Louisa said, politely.

"But I've done nothing."

"You arranged everything for our arrival," Barbara said.

"So don't you think that it's only fair for Barbara to take care of our departure?"

"I never looked at it that way," Sadie said. "Seems sort of odd to look at it that way."

"Oh," Barbara said, smiling and looking straight into Louisa's open eyes, "Louisa tends to make symbols out of just about anything."

Louisa laughed. "To a fault."

"Yes," Barbara agreed, but without any bitterness, "to a fault. So," she turned to face Sadie, "it's settled?"

"But—"

"Yes, it's settled," Louisa said firmly.

"And when I pack up the things on the first floor, I'll make sure that the portrait goes to the right owner." Barbara looked at Sadie, hoping Sadie would smile.

But Sadie didn't smile. Her hands flew to her head. "Oh, no, no! I wouldn't let you send it, not anywhere. You can't send it—"

"You mean you want to take it with you?"

"Yes, yes," Sadie said. Her hands flew down and opened up to embrace Barbara.

"Don't," Barbara said, holding her hand in the air between them. "That's not necessary."

Louisa looked at the boat of souls. Sadie's hands descended to her lap. Barbara, readjusting her hair, found that she was looking at the boat.

The boat sat still and moved in both directions. The Code could not tell you if the boat were going to heaven or to hell; up or down; in or out; with or against the tide. The Code could not tell you whether the souls were leaving or coming. And the Code could not tell you whether the cry from the open mouth of the man at the stern—or the bow—was the same cry as the cry from the open mouth of the man at the bow, or the stern; whose voice cried damnation, whose voice cried resurrection; whose voice belonged to whom.

Sitting still, it moved in both directions no matter whose eyes looked at it.

GONE

(Epilogue)

"WHAT HAS SHE GOT?" GEORGE SAID, LOOKING OUT OF HIS living room window. He rose from his chair, put his newspaper on the table (a mosaic made by his second daughter) and went to the front door.

"George! George! Help me," Sadie said, rushing and sliding on the walk. Seeing her husband open the door, she turned in the other direction back to her car.

"Hello, dahlin'," George said, reaching over to kiss his wife.

"Oh, George, look!"

"Yes, honey, I see it. But what is it?"

"It's the portrait, it's the portrait."

"Of Mother?"

"Who else?" Sadie looked at him. "Here, we've got to get it inside. The moving men were so nice. They packed it and loaded it onto the car and all while I was teaching this morning, and when I came back to pick it up, well, I— We've got to get it inside."

George stood looking at the large crate. "Well, honey. I imagine it took a few moving men to lift it. I don't think we can do it ourselves."

"But of course we can. We've—"

"Now, just be patient."

"Are the girls home?" Sadie said, flying up the walk, slipping in the snow on her heels. "Girls! Girls!" George began to follow his wife.

"They're not home," he said. Sadie stopped suddenly, and slipped. George grabbed her just before she fell. They stood still, looking into each other's faces. George cleared his throat. Sadie flushed. Neither knew what to say to the other. Sadie looked at her husband, then back at the crate on the roof of the car, then back to her husband.

"Oh, honey," she said. "I've got so much to tell you I don't know where to begin. We've got to—you know," Sadie squeezed George's arm. "Mother finally gave the portrait to— well," she stopped. "It was very complicated. It was just so very complicated."

"What was, honey?" He tried to lead her into the house. Sadie took a few steps, then stopped and turned.

"Why, everything, just everything! But mostly—George, can't we try to get the portrait inside?"

"Inside?"

"Yes."

"I think maybe we'll have to wait until the girls get home. We should all be able to carry it in."

"When will that be?"

George looked at his watch. "Pretty soon." He again tried to lead his wife into their house, but she tugged his arm.

"We can't just leave it. Someone might steal it."

"We can watch from the window," George said calmly. "Nobody's going to take it."

Finally George was able to negotiate Sadie along the slippery walk and up the stairs into their house. Sitting on the couch, facing George but keeping an eye on the car, Sadie began. "Oh, dear," she said. "I don't know where we're going to fit everything! But," she stopped—"we'll make room."

"Yes, honey," George said.

"And this room," Sadie looked around, "this room where we are right now, it will be completely different," she said. "It will look exactly—exactly like Mother's living room."

"Well, now, I don't quite see how it can look exactly the same," George said.

"Oh, no, honey. You'll see." George looked skeptically at their living room, and then with resignation he looked at his familiar fluffy wife.

"We'll see," he said.

"Well," Barbara said at the door of Mother's house. "I guess that's it." She turned to Tom who stood beside her in the doorway. It was Thursday. They had been helping the moving company since Monday afternoon when Tom arrived. "The property's all accounted for." They stepped inside out of the cold, and, forgetting that there was nothing for them to sit on, they sat down on the stairs. They were waiting for a cab to take them to the airport.

"Did you pack all your things?" Tom said.

"Yes," Barbara replied. "Tom—"

"Yes?"

"Thank you for helping me."

"Oh, Barbara, don't think of it. It would have been impossible to do alone. I never realized your family had so many things."

Barbara put her hand affectionately on her husband's shoulder. "Neither did I, really, until now." She removed her hand. "You know, Tom. I haven't even begun to think of where we're going to put everything once it arrives. I tried to think, when we were grabbing it, but I couldn't think of everything all at once."

"There's nothing to worry about," Tom said. "When we get home we'll take a good look and see what we want to do."

"You don't—mind?" Barbara said softly.

"Mind?" Tom turned to face his wife. "Mind what?"

"Well, all of these things in our house, you know. I think that—well, we didn't build our house for this kind of furniture," Barbara said.

"Good furniture is good furniture," Tom said. "It doesn't make any difference what its age or style if it is good furniture. And your parents collected very good pieces."

Outside there was a honk. Tom stood up and reached for his and Barbara's coats. As he put his wife's coat around her shoulders he rested his hands on them and said, "You were right, you know."

"About what?" Barbara turned to stand facing him. He held her.

"About the love letters," he said. "It must have been difficult to persuade Sadie. But it was the right thing to do."

"Thank you," Barbara said. She kissed him. Looking into her husband's face, Barbara suddenly smiled. "You know," she said, "Mother was right."

"About what?"

"Your eyes are too close together."

He turned to open the door, laughing. "Your mother did have a way with words."

"Yes, she did," Barbara said, locking the door behind her.

She then took the keys and placed them in an envelope in the mailbox for Sadie to pick up later.

Their flight left on schedule.

Louisa opened the door. "Hello? Is anybody home?"

"Louisa? Is that you?" she heard Patrick call from upstairs. "You're home earlier than I expected," he said, coming down the stairs to kiss her.

"Oh, well, I drove pretty fast. And I'm freezing cold. I need some coffee or something." They went into the kitchen and turned on the lights.

"Where are the boys?" she said when the coffee was made.

"They went out somewhere. They should be back before midnight," Patrick said. He waited for his wife to speak.

"Here," Louisa said. She reached into her pocketbook and took out the netsuke. "Look at this." She handed it to Patrick. He took it and held it in his hand; then he held either end with the tips of his fingers.

"What is it?"

"It's a Buddhist talisman of some kind. Which way do you think it's going?" She smiled.

"Oh, from left to right," Patrick said.

"Look again." He stared at the boat.

"Well, right to left," he laughed, and put the boat down. "But this isn't all you've got to show, is it?" he teased.

"No," Louisa said, placing the boat between them. "The rest of the stuff—Patrick, there's a lot of things that will be arriving soon."

"Well," Patrick sat back, "I guess it's fortunate that our house is too large, then." He waited a moment, not knowing what to ask, or if he should ask. Then he leaned forward. "What happened?"

Louisa paused and looked at her husband. She did not know what to say. "I," she began. Then, suddenly, "I lost what I found. No, no—I mean, I found what I lost," she said, and grabbed her husband's hand.

HB6H